James Nora MD

THE BIOLOGY
OF TISSUE
TRANSPLANTATION

NEW ENGLAND JOURNAL OF MEDICINE

MEDICAL PROGRESS SERIES

THE BIOLOGY
OF TISSUE
TRANSPLANTATION

PAUL S. RUSSELL, M.D.

JOHN HOMANS PROFESSOR OF SURGERY,
HARVARD MEDICAL SCHOOL;
CHIEF OF THE GENERAL SURGICAL SERVICES,
MASSACHUSETTS GENERAL HOSPITAL

ANTHONY P. MONACO, M.D.

INSTRUCTOR IN SURGERY,
HARVARD MEDICAL SCHOOL;
ASSISTANT IN SURGERY,
MASSACHUSETTS GENERAL HOSPITAL

Illustrations by
Sidney J. Rosenthal

LITTLE, BROWN AND COMPANY
BOSTON

THIS MONOGRAPH FIRST APPEARED AS A MEDICAL PROGRESS REPORT
IN THE NEW ENGLAND JOURNAL OF MEDICINE.
PUBLICATION IN BOOK FORM INCORPORATES ADDITIONAL MATERIAL AND
THE ADDITION OF ILLUSTRATIONS.

Published in Great Britain
by J. & A. Churchill Ltd., London

PRINTED IN THE UNITED STATES OF AMERICA

PREFACE

Although it is not apparent what place transplantation will ultimately deserve in the armamentarium of the clinical surgeon, the sweep of possibilities which this new approach offers is immense. In any case, the growing dependence of surgery upon some of the flourishing younger sciences is particularly clear in this field, and it is equally apparent that surgeons can only maintain familiarity with the sciences upon which they must constantly draw by making their own attempts to contribute to them in return.

We shall not apologize, therefore, for venturing beyond the bounds sometimes set for surgery, but cannot be excused any of our shortcomings by pleading the scientific innocence often attributed to clinicians.

It is hoped that this book may prove interesting not only to surgeons and other clinicians but to other biologists who have a common interest in events which reflect the specificity of living cells.

The contents of this book originally appeared in serial form in the *New England Journal of Medicine* beginning in September, 1964. A discussion of the statistical analysis of the survival of human renal allografts has been included in the present text through the courtesy of Dr. Benjamin A. Barnes. A number of illustrations, for which the authors are indebted to Mr. Sidney J. Rosenthal, have been added.

Preface

The work of gathering the contents of this book was supported in part by grants (AM-07055, HE-06664, T4-CA-5018 and FR-05182) from the United States Public Health Service and by the William F. Milton Fund.

We acknowledge gratefully the devoted help of Miss Lizabeth Simonds and Miss Joan Hunter with the manuscript, of Miss Genevieve Cole with the references, and of Miss Margaret Wilkie and Miss Mary L. Wood with the proofreading of the final text.

P. S. R.
A. P. M.

Boston

CONTENTS

vii

Contents

THE BIOLOGY
OF TISSUE
TRANSPLANTATION

1

INTRODUCTION AND TERMINOLOGY

I F the common phenomenon of fertilization is excepted it can be said that the transplantation of living cells from one individual to another is not a natural event. Indeed, from time immemorial the junction of portions of separate individuals was considered the special province of supernatural forces or deities inspired by dreams of the remarkable qualities that might be expected in creatures having capabilities normally beyond the power of a single species. The preoccupation of the ancients with such dreams was certainly great, so that the modern world has inherited not only the remains of legions of sphinxes and other beasts, fashioned in metal or stone by men as copies of divine workmanship, but also a rich array of legends concerning the exploits of everything from mermaids to chimeras.* Man's attempts to produce living individuals, embodying the tissues of others, by

---

*Gr. Myth. A she monster represented as vomiting flames and, usually, as having a lion's head, goat's body and dragon's or serpent's tail; it was killed by Bellerophon. Biol. A mixture of tissues of different genetic constitution in the same part of an organism.

transplantation methods, likewise go back many centuries.

Sporadic efforts to rectify certain physiologic deficits in clinical medicine by transplantation of the appropriate living tissue have long been made. Tissue transplantation has occupied an important place in the armamentarium of the experimental biologist and for a long time has been of central importance to embryologic research and in many investigations in the field of cancer. In about the past twenty years, however, understanding of the laws governing the survival or failure of foreign cells has increased immensely. Tracing the origins of this modern rush of activity and knowledge, the substantial contributions of a few, particularly in the field of tumor transplantation, must be gratefully acknowledged. Jensen, Tyzzer, J. B. Murphy, Leo Loeb and C. C. Little should receive special mention. More recently, the late Peter Gorer and George Snell have played central parts in establishing the new science of transplantation biology. Particular recognition of the discoveries of P. B. Medawar and his colleagues is also due since it was he who first consciously set out in systematic fashion to elucidate by a series of experiments, elegant in their simplicity, the laws of behavior of normal tissues transplanted between laboratory animals of ordinary genetic diversity.

Although in very recent years some success has been achieved in turning the impressive new knowledge gained from the experimental laboratories to various clinical uses it should also be emphasized that the new science of transplantation biology "offers one of the few negotiable pathways into the central regions of biology"[1] and that its influence has been a particularly healthy one, tending to unify many of the traditional clinical realms with genetics, embryology, immunology and ultrastructural studies — to mention a few — in a new dynamic interdependence.

It will thus be utterly impossible to attempt a thorough account, in limited space, of the far-flung activities that could be considered to bear directly on the biology of tissue transplantation. For example, much of the important investigations utilizing tumors in transplantation, with the exception of immunologic enhancement, must be entirely excluded. We can also include nothing of advances in methods of tissue preservation, which is certainly a closely allied activity. We shall concentrate on progress since the last account of the subject appeared in the *New England Journal of Medicine* in 1956,[2] but can find little comfort in this seemingly circumscribed task, which will still allow us to do no more than point out major sectors of activity and interest, excusing ourselves from any attempt at an exhaustive review even of those.

Attention should be called to two volumes on the subject of tissue transplantation that have recently appeared.[3,4] The proceedings of several recent conferences, and a number of recent reviews, will be mentioned appropriately.

Terminology

There has been much debate and not a little confusion over the terminology that will prove to be most appropriate and informative in the field of transplantation. Current usage, which is becoming ever more familiar to veterans in transplantation research, retains the not inconsiderable drawbacks of being etymologically incorrect and at the same time quite inconsistent with long established immunologic terms. For these reasons there has been some move to alter the terminology to remove these objections, moves that have been somewhat more successful in the "old world" than in the "new." P. A. Gorer first publicly called attention to this need[5] and later re-emphasized it.[6] It has also been championed by Medawar[7] and by G. D. Snell.[8] The favored new terms in Table 1 are directly derived from Gorer and are consistent with those favored by Snell.

Other useful terms commonly employed are *orthotopic* to describe a graft, of any genetic origin, that is placed in the anatomic position normally occupied by

TABLE 1. *Terminology of Tissue Transplantation.*

OLD TERMINOLOGY	NEW TERMINOLOGY	NEW ADJECTIVE	DEFINITION
Autograft	*Autograft*	*Autologous*	Graft in which donor is also recipient
Isograft	*Isograft*	*Isogeneic*	Graft between individuals identical in histocompatibility antigens
Homograft	*Allograft*	*Allogeneic*	Graft between genetically dissimilar members of same species
Heterograft	*Xenograft*	*Xenogeneic*	Graft between species

such tissue — for example, a kidney in the renal fossa, with appropriate anastomoses at the renal pedicle, or a skin graft placed to a recipient site in the skin. *Heterotopic* grafts are all those in unnatural recipient locations.

A further set of descriptive terms, introduced by Longmire,[9] has been of particular value to surgeons. These terms, as originally proposed, were *homostatic* and *homovital*. They defined the expected or intended functional capacity of tissues used in reconstructive surgery, the homostatic being a graft derived from an individual of the same species as the recipient but deprived of viability in processing, such as a preserved arterial graft. Homostatic grafts are intended to serve a mechanical function after transplantation that does not require viability. Such grafts often act as a scaffold or matrix into which host tissues gradually extend by a process of creeping substitution. Homovital grafts or transplants are expected to perform their full, normal metabolic function after transfer. The new terminology would, of course, alter these words to *allostatic* and *allovital* in conformity with the other terms.

2

THE NATURE OF THE REACTION

IT is still surprising to some to learn that allogeneic grafts survive initially in full vigor by both morphologic and functional criteria in a state entirely indistinguishable from autografts. This important fact, clearly discerned by the Danish biologist C. O. Jensen in his work with transplants of malignant tumors, goes a long way toward ruling out Ehrlich's notion that inevitable differences in chemical constituents between individuals, even of the same species, could account for the death of transplanted tissues on a purely nutritional basis. Actually, if certain straightforward requisites are fulfilled, such as provision for an adequate blood supply before the death of the transplanted cells by ischemia, the complex process underlying the active rejection of a graft by its host usually requires at least a few days to become manifest, thus ruling out any sort of "built-in" or "ready-made" response already existent in the previously untreated recipient. Nevertheless, this temporary period of grace is soon over, so that the usual allogeneic graft — for example, a skin graft between randomly selected adult rabbits — will begin to show signs of inflammation by the fourth or fifth day, which rapidly progress in the presence of an increasingly dense leukocytic infiltrate, ending in complete necrosis of the entire graft by about the ninth day.[10] Medawar's truly classic description of the rejection of full-thickness allogeneic skin grafts in rabbits, along with much other information, indicates that this complex response draws upon the participation of inflammatory cells, lymphatic and blood vessels and very possibly humoral factors to overturn the progress of normal healing, which normally works toward the incorporation of the grafted tissue into its new host.

There is now no doubt that the rejection process, however complex, is set in motion and directed by immunologic mechanisms. This is most clearly demonstrated by the "second-set phenomenon,"[11] in which a second graft from the same donor, or from an individual of identical genetic constitution, is rejected in an accelerated, and much more violent, fashion (Fig. 1). A major subject of investigation and debate is the question of whether the vectors of the specific immune response are activated migratory leukocytes,

---

FIGURE 1. *First- and Second-Set Rejection.*

In the upper portion of this figure an A/Jax mouse has received a full-thickness skin allograft from a C57BL/6 donor with prompt rejection at 10 days ("first-set" rejection). These animals differ at the "strong" H-2 genetic locus.

Below, a C57BL/6 mouse donates a skin graft, liver slice, or lymph node cell suspension to different A/Jax recipients. A subsequent C57BL/6 test skin graft placed 10 days later is fully rejected in each case by 6 days in accelerated fashion ("second-set" rejection).

This illustrates the general principle of wide sharing of individual specific antigens. One tissue is capable of sensitizing a recipient against a later graft of the same or another tissue (certain exceptions to this are discussed in the text).

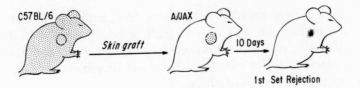

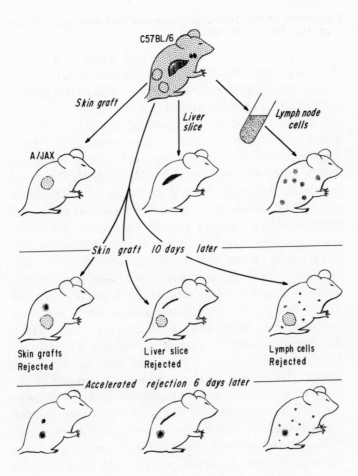

which may or may not release free antibody in the immediate vicinity of the graft, specially constructed globulin molecules fashioned by certain cells and released at a distance from the graft or some combination of these possibilities.

Evocation of the Immune Response and the Importance of the Recipient Site

The evocation and persistence of specific sensitivity by transplanted allogeneic cells depends heavily upon the avenue of access of the grafted cells to the immunologically responsive centers of the host. With the use of the second-set rejection of test skin grafts of donor origin as a measure of prior sensitization by a graft of living dissociated donor cells it can be shown that sensitivity varies considerably with the route of injection. Although there is some species variation, in general the intraperitoneal and intradermal routes are roughly similar, giving rapidly detectable sensitivity (two or three days), whereas the subcutaneous and intravenous routes are much less effective.[12,13] The immunity resulting from the rejection of such dissociated cell grafts is much shorter lived, usually no more than a few weeks, than that resulting from the rejection of a fixed tissue graft, such as a skin graft. Here, the immune state is readily detectable at virtually full force for at least a year and may persist much longer. In general, grafts between individuals of the same mammalian species of ordinary genetic diversity are fully rejected in two weeks or less. Since the full immunologic response of the recipient is apparently called forth to meet the challenge under these circumstances, the variation in survival time is quite narrow, no more than a day or so.[14] Increasing the amount of tissue grafted over a fairly wide range influences the survival time only slightly in such experiments[10] although some Russian workers have described prolonged survival of massive skin grafts occupying a third of the body surface in rats of undefined genetic diversity.[15] This finding has been confirmed in mice, in which it occurs only in animals with no more than slightly differing quotas of transplantation or histocompatibility antigens.[16] A recent study in rats[17] has confirmed that if strong genetic differences exist between the animals studied, no significant change in allograft survival time in relation to graft size is found.

The question of the mechanism of expression of an immune state directed toward the antigen or antigens possessed by grafted foreign cells, but absent from their host, will be discussed below. Although many important questions remain concerning this "efferent limb" of the immunologic arc, very little reliable information is available concerning the course of events along the "afferent limb." It is known that an allogeneic graft will soon provoke the presence of large, pyronin-positive, mononuclear cells in regional lymph nodes that appear to be a direct response to the presence of the graft.[18] The fact that specific reactivity appears first in regional lymph nodes draining allogeneic grafts, as the ingenious and important experiments of Mitchison demonstrated,[19] suggests a regional immunologic transaction that precedes the more readily demonstrable generalized state of hypersensitivity. If the large antigenic molecules concerned are actually released from a graft, as they seem to be from certain cultured cells,[20] and traverse lymphatic or other channels to the regional lymph nodes without losing their specificity, one would expect that allogeneic grafts, even when contained in the cell impermeable filter chambers devised by Algire, would release their appropriate antigens and sensitize the host. Algire[21] denied that they do, and some experiments of Russell and Sparrow[22] confirm this. The question remains open to further study. The possibility that specific antigens are actually carried by wandering cells from graft to reactive centers is reasonable, although no direct evidence of its occurrence in vivo exists, and would be consistent with the attractive concept of Fishman, gained from in vitro experiments, that antigen must be "processed" by macrophages before being passed on to lymphoid cells, where specific antibody production can begin.[23] Several experiments[24-26] in which the time of residence of skin grafts on a foreign host that is required for sensitization to result, and for reactive cells in the lymphoid centers to appear, are also consistent with this scheme. Since sensitization is detectable coincidentally with the first formation of open blood and lymphatic channels, which develop no sooner than about forty-eight hours after grafting, these pathways can be assumed to favor the return passage of antigen either in the free state or cell bound. Vascular channels may not be critically necessary for sensitization, however, since it could be detected in three or four days even when grafts were repeatedly removed and replaced, with consequent destruction of developing vascular channels.[24]

At any rate, in contrast to grafts of dissociated cells, the weight of evidence suggests that all grafts of organized tissues (with certain exceptions mentioned below), which rapidly receive a normal blood supply from the host, can be expected both to provoke and succumb to the maximal reaction that the recipient is capable of raising against the dose of foreign tissue involved. Bits of organized tissue transferred as free implants to, for example, the subcutaneous region, or into the substance of a muscle, will gain a full host blood supply in three to five days. Central necrosis can be expected if such fragments exceed approximately 1 mm. in diameter, since the newly acquired vascular supply will not reach internal cells soon enough to prevent necrosis in larger fragments.[27] A direct blood supply is not, perhaps, altogether necessary for rejection to occur since free grafts of small sheets of enzymatically separated pure epidermis, laid upon an open recipient site in the integument of an allogeneic rabbit, are rejected, although with a survival time slightly longer than that expected of intact skin grafts.[28,29]

Nevertheless, the nature of the potential for vascular connections between host and graft, both blood and lymphatic, may be of considerable importance in determining the several sites that have been demonstrated to present special environments particularly favorable to foreign graft survival.

The *anterior chamber of the eye* has been recognized at least since 1873[30] as a favorable site for graft survival. This small space, bathed with cell-free fluid, seems to be in general more hospitable to malignant[31] and perhaps embryonic[32] than to normal adult tissues. Although the evidence is not yet clear, it presently favors the interpretation that foreign (that is, allogeneic or xenogeneic) tissues tend to survive because of a privilege that is owed to their diminished ability to incite an immunologic reaction rather than to their being exempt from an existing immune state. Thus, surviving adrenocortical allografts between mouse strains in the anterior chamber can be killed by an intraperitoneal injection of spleen cells from the donor strain that provoke a vigorous reaction to donor specific antigens, even those confined in the anterior chamber.[33] The importance to survival of the development of a direct blood supply from the iris to grafts in the anterior chamber has not been finally established. Medawar[34] found vascularization to be a premonitory sign of rejection with allogeneic skin grafts placed in the anterior chamber of the rabbit, whereas the Woodruffs[35] observed rich vascularization in long surviving thyroid allografts in rats. They believe that a gradual process of "adaptation" (discussed at greater length in the section Graft Adaptation in Chapter 3) of such grafts to their hosts can develop and that vascularization of adapted grafts need not interfere with their survival.

The *substantia propria of the cornea* is likewise a privileged site of great clinical utility. Here, there is agreement that vascularization of corneal grafts is accompanied by rejection and that prior sensitization with donor tissues prevents acceptance of the graft.[36,37]

The area within the *meninges of the brain* has long been known to be a relatively privileged site, although probably somewhat less so than the anterior chamber of the eye. It was recognized some time ago[38] that such grafts, to defy successfully the usual fate of allogeneic tissue, must lie wholly within the meninges and not impinge upon the ventricles. Again, the importance of vascularization of such grafts is not finally settled, although the present evidence favors the view that survival depends upon a lack of direct vascular supply.[34]

The *testis* is another site in which foreign grafts enjoy relatively favored survival. This was first determined by workers in the field of tumor transplantation, but the hospitality extends in some degree to normal tissues. Small implants of normal tissues may survive and, where appropriate, carry on detectable physiologic functions, as in endocrine allografts, for periods ranging up to two or more times their expected survival when placed intramuscularly or subcutaneously.[33,39] No systematic study of the importance of the presence or absence of a direct blood vascular supply has been made for grafts in this location. The only explanation for its special qualities has been laid to the unusual anatomy of the lymphatic drainage of the testis, traversing the retroperitoneum as it does, to the level of the kidneys before encountering its first regular sentinel lymph node.

The *cheek pouch of the hamster* has received much attention as an especially favored location for tumor transplant growth, even including xenografts. Grafts are usually placed beneath the stratified epithelium lining this distensible evagination of the buccal cavity onto a well vascularized layer of connective tissue that is fairly dense. Here, they promptly gain a rich blood supply and may persist for very long periods in good condition. A state of systemic sensitivity to tissues of donor origin will disallow graft persistence, however, and a skin graft from the same donor placed elsewhere on a recipient currently supporting the growth of tissue in the cheek pouch will bring about the rejection of the favored graft as it is itself destroyed. An elegant analysis of this important curiosity has been performed by Billingham and Silvers.[40] They concluded that the connective-tissue layer of the pouch wall is somehow endowed with the property of impeding the afferent side of the immunologic response since free grafts of cheek-pouch wall, including the connective-tissue layer, were usually accepted for long periods on the body surface of other individuals. Other examples of an immunologic insulating effect provided by connective tissue have not been identified, but it seems at least possible, in the light of these observations, that some similar mechanism could be at work where certain existing autoantigens are believed to be compartmentalized within the adult body — for example, in the thyroid gland and brain — and that autosensitization may normally be discouraged by this form of segregation.

There may, of course, be additional sites affording the privilege of relatively extended survival on other grounds. It has recently been found, for example, in our laboratory that parathyroid allografts in rats placed within the substance of the thymus enjoy a systematically prolonged survival over those placed in the substance of a muscle, which, in turn, outlive those placed within the spleen.[39]

Participation of Cells

It has been widely held that the presence of leukocytic inflammatory cells of recipient origin in the immediate vicinity of a graft of organized tissue is the most characteristic histologic feature of the rejection process. In fact, J. B. Murphy's admirable work established this important connection almost forty years ago.[41] In initial grafts, made to previously unsensitized recipients, infiltrating cells are commonly first seen by the second or third day. They rapidly increase in number in skin grafts and, though finding their way to all parts of the graft, tend to congregate at the graft-host interface. Vascular obstruction may occur, but it is a late phenomenon in the "first-set" reaction, where it can hardly explain the often extensive death of graft cells that, by then, has already taken place. In the "second-set" reaction, where the recipient has been sensitized by rejecting a previous graft of donor origin, the process takes on much greater violence, and all its features are accelerated. The concentration of cells at the graft-host junction is often much greater, giving rise, for example, in rabbit skin grafts to a typical "black band" of cells that can be seen grossly on the stained histologic slide.[10] A special form of the accelerated rejection process in skin grafts has been described as the "white-graft reaction."[42] This apt label has been given to the course of certain second grafts, applied within a very few days after complete rejection of a prior graft from the donor, which remain pallid and inert on their beds, never gaining a blood supply before becoming necrotic. Here, vascular obstruction on an immunologic basis leads the infiltrative cellular response almost entirely, and the graft dies an ischemic death with almost no visible inflammatory cells within it.

Although the percentage of different types of leukocytes varies at different stages of graft rejection and in different species, the infiltrate proves to be composed of a mixture of cell types, including polymorphonuclear cells, particularly in its early days. Eosinophils in moderate numbers are also present, particularly in the rabbit, but the predominant cells are mononuclear. By light microscopy the commonest cell approximates a small lymphocyte in appearance[10] although the higher magnification of electron microscopy shows this group of cells to be composed of a variety of mononuclear forms, usually with few mitochondria and a small complement of endoplasmic reticulum.[29] Plasma cells are typically present in the later stages of the rejection process but are comparatively rare.

Gorer made the important discovery that cytotoxic humoral antibodies directed toward cells from the donor can be regularly demonstrated in the serum after the height of allograft rejection.[43,44] Although this observation has been amply confirmed the most telling evidence in favor of cellular participation in graft rejection remains that of Mitchison and Dube,[45] who showed that specific sensitivity to grafts of organized tissues can be readily transferred by means of lymphoid cells from one individual to another but not by means of serum, even when comparatively high

---

FIGURE 2. *Transfer of Allograft Immunity ("Adoptively Acquired Immunity").*

A C57BL/6 mouse donates a skin allograft to a mouse of the A/Jax strain. This graft is rejected. The recipient animal is then bled and the serum recovered. The lymph nodes and spleen of the recipient are also excised and a lymphoid cell suspension prepared. The serum is then injected into a normal adult A/Jax mouse and the cell suspension injected into a second A/Jax animal. Three days later both animals receive a first-set C57BL/6 skin allograft. After 6 days the graft donated to the A/Jax animal which received the cell suspension has undergone accelerated rejection while the one on the serum-treated animal is still viable and goes on to a first-set rejection.

This experiment emphasizes that allograft immunity can be readily transferred by cells but not by serum; i.e. it is a cell-mediated type of immunity rather than one dependent on humoral antibody.

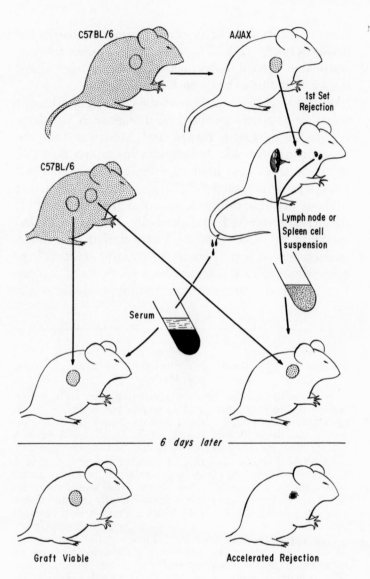

C57BL/6

A/JAX

1st Set Rejection

Lymph node or Spleen cell suspension

C57BL/6

Serum

6 days later

Graft Viable

Accelerated Rejection

titers of antibody activity can be demonstrated in the donor serum[46] (Fig. 2). Essentially similar findings from the careful experiments of Lawrence[47] have shown that this extends to human beings.

Further evidence to support the concept of allograft rejection as a cell-mediated phenomenon is the demonstration by Brent, Brown and Medawar that the reaction against skin homografts in guinea pigs can be made to express itself as a typical "delayed-type" hypersensitivity reaction[48,49] (Fig. 3). When living cells, or cell-free antigenic material from a skin-graft donor, are injected intradermally into a sensitized recipient, a "direct reaction," very similar to a tuberculin reaction, is provoked. A "transfer reaction" results when cells from regional lymph nodes of a sensitized recipient are injected intradermally into the

---

FIGURE 3. *The Direct and Transfer Reactions of Brent, Brown, and Medawar.*[48,49]

I. *The Direct Reaction.* A sensitizing skin graft is first transferred from guinea pig A to guinea pig B. Following its rejection, donor lymph node cells from guinea pig A are injected intradermally into guinea pig B. In 24 to 48 hours a typical delayed skin reaction is visible at the injection site.

II. *The Transfer Reaction.* Following the rejection of a skin graft from guinea pig A by guinea pig B, recipient lymph node cells from regional lymph nodes of the sensitized recipient (guinea pig B) are injected intradermally into the donor (guinea pig A). In 24 to 48 hours a delayed skin reaction is visible.

The *direct reaction* depends upon the rapid mobilization of sensitized cells in the previously grafted recipient as an accelerated host-versus-graft reaction at the injection site. The *transfer reaction* depends upon a reaction by the injected, sensitized donor cells against immediately adjacent recipient antigens as a local graft-versus-host reaction.

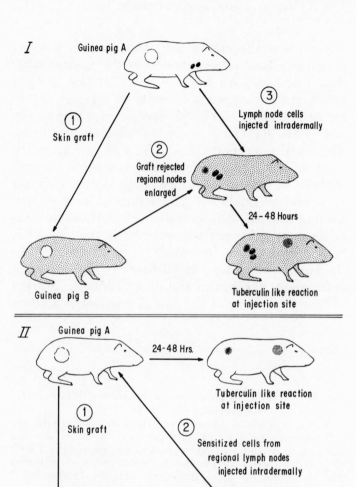

I

Guinea pig A

① Skin graft

② Graft rejected regional nodes enlarged

③ Lymph node cells injected intradermally

Guinea pig B

24 - 48 Hours

Tuberculin like reaction at injection site

II

Guinea pig A

24 - 48 Hrs.

Tuberculin like reaction at injection site

① Skin graft

② Sensitized cells from regional lymph nodes injected intradermally

Guinea pig B

Graft rejected

original skin allograft donor. This reaction is interpreted as a local passive transfer of the reactive state. Both reactions have a latent period of five to eight hours, reach maximum intensity in twenty-four to forty-eight hours, are highly specific immunologically and persist for many weeks like allograft sensitivity. The transfer reaction can also be mediated by leukocytes or peritoneal exudate cells, but not by serum. Viability of cells is obligatory. Both reactions appear to depend essentially upon some form of local engagement of antigen with sensitized cells. Although cutaneous reactivity is not demonstrable in the mouse[49] it can be achieved in the rabbit[50,51] and in man.[52] In the latter species, the "recall flare"[42] (Fig. 4) — an erythema at the healed site of a previously rejected allograft appearing at the time of rejection of a subse-

---

FIGURE 4. *Allograft Sensitization in Man. "White graft" rejection and the "recall flare."*

Initial skin grafts between randomly selected adults are fully rejected by 8 to 15 days *(above)*. A second-set skin graft 10 days later undergoes accelerated rejection in 4 to 7 days and provokes an associated recrudescence of erythema and induration in the initial graft site, the "recall flare" *(middle)*.

If the second graft is placed less than 7 days after rejection of the first graft, the second graft fails to become vascularized and is rejected as a "white graft" *(lower)*.

The "recall flare" is believed to be due to persisting antigens of donor origin at the site of the first graft to which the heightened sensitivity induced by the second graft is directed.

"White graft" rejection is thought to be a manifestation of a very high level of sensitivity which has prevented vascularization of the second graft.

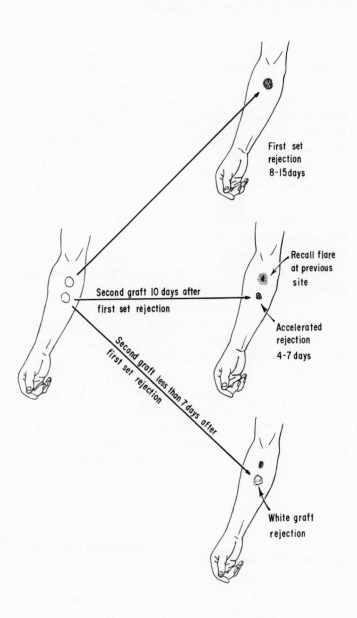

First set
rejection
8-15 days

Second graft 10 days after
first set rejection

Recall flare
at previous
site

Accelerated
rejection
4-7 days

Second graft less than 7 days after
first set rejection

White graft
rejection

quent allograft — is probably a similar example of the cutaneous expression of allograft sensitivity.

Another line of evidence that has been thought to be important in supporting the necessity for close contact between reactive cells and graft is that of Weaver, Algire and Prehn.[53] These well known experiments, in which the cell impermeable filter-chamber technic was utilized by its originators, demonstrated that allogeneic cells could withstand the deleterious effects of serologic antibody, which was believed to be freely admitted to the interior of the chamber, so long as they were sheltered from direct contact with recipient leukocytes. This was reported to be true even when the recipient had previously been sensitized to donor tissues by prior rejection of an appropriate graft.

Although there is good reason to think that circumstances can be contrived in which responsibility for graft damage can be ascribed solely to serologic antibody (as discussed below) the available evidence continues to favor a single general mode of reaction mediated in some way by cells. There has been much recent progress in analysis of the cellular events involved, some of it summarized in a recent conference bearing on the subject.[54] A particularly knotty and important question is that of the specificity of the cells that gather about a graft at the time of its destruction. Does this population include[55] "innocent bystanders enveloped by a humoral antibody they never made, other cells engaged full tilt in fabricating and secreting antibody into their environs and still other cells synthesizing antibody but unable or unwilling to relinquish it"? Recent studies in which radioactively labeled lymphoid cells from specifically sensitized individuals are followed after transfer to a second recipient at about the time it receives a graft (or other appropriate antigenic stimulus) from the original donor have revealed that the transferred cells comprise a surprisingly *small* proportion of the migratory cellular population at the site of the graft toward which their sensitivity was directed.[56,57] This appears to have been confirmed with similar technics in single animals where the maneuver of cell transfer was unnecessary.[58] The evidence presently available, therefore, does not cast serious doubt upon the importance of the presence of cells to the rejection process but does question whether they arrive by virtue of a specificity assigned to them by adherent humoral antibody produced by other cells or by the receipt of certain subcellular components that direct them to specific action.

Participation of Humoral Antibody

It is perhaps arbitrary and certainly difficult to separate considerations of the cellular from the humoral factors that may be involved in graft rejection, and no implication of a necessary biologic separation between the two is implied by the fact that we here devote a separate section to work done with an eye toward humoral mechanisms. Within the past few years the question of the active and unaided participation of humoral antibody in allograft rejection has received considerable interest. Stetson has recently reviewed the subject.[59] Since the histocompatibility isoantigens are best defined in the mouse, studies of the antibody response in inbred mice to isoimmunization have been particularly plentiful and rewarding. The isoantibodies to the strong H-2 isoantigens (see Chapter 4) have been carefully investigated. It has now been generally recognized that antibody production is probably an almost invariable consequence of the allotransplantation of skin or other normal tissues, as well as neoplasms. The antibodies thus formed are, of course, directed against histocompatibility isoantigens present in donor tissue and absent from the host, and may be detected by hemagglutination,[60] leukocyte agglutination,[61] hemolysis[62] or a variety of cytotoxic reactions.[63,64] Stetson has emphasized the point that serologic methods now available lack sensitivity and are often inadequate for the detection of low titers of antibody after the application of a single allograft.[59] In addition to the mouse ample evidence of specific antibody formation in response to allografting has been found in rats,[65] rabbits,[64,66,67] dogs,[68] guinea pigs,[69] man[70] and numerous other species, including reptiles[71] and fish.[72]

Kinetic studies in mice[73,74] and chickens[75] indicate that the primary humoral response after initial exposure to histocompatibility antigens, although weak, is detectable within four days, and reaches a peak by two or three weeks. Subsequent exposures result in secondary responses to higher titers. Stetson and Jensen[76] obtained evidence that antibody appearing after secondary exposure was of the 7S gammaglobulin variety, and these authors suggest the possibility that antibody following primary immunization is of the 19S type. In view of the differences between the biologic properties of 7S and 19S gamma globulins Stetson[59] has pointed out the need for a thorough study of this aspect of the isoantibody response.

The widely shared skepticism regarding the significance of humoral antibody in allograft rejection has been based on three general areas of experimentation:

the early failure of attempts to detect humoral hemagglutinating antibody[77] and cytotoxic antibody[78,79] during skin-graft rejection in rabbits; the experiments of Algire,[21,80] mentioned above, in which allografts enclosed in Millipore chambers, permitting passage of humoral but not cellular elements, survived for long periods, even when placed in a previously immunized host; and repeated failure to transfer allograft sensitivity by large doses of serum in a number of species.[81,46] The first of these objections, as indicated above, is no longer tenable.

Subsequent studies of certain types of allografts in diffusion chambers have also rendered Algire's original conclusions less compelling. Apparently, humoral antibody and complement penetrate such chambers with difficulty,[82] and when they do so in appropriate levels, some allogeneic grafts are destroyed. This is true for leukemic cells[83] and for grafts of mouse fibroblasts.[84] Algire, in his last published work,[85] reported that neoplastic cells of the plasma-cell series were destroyed in chambers whereas non-neoplastic donor cells survived. Apparently, not all graft cells are equally susceptible to destruction in the Millipore chamber, an observation substantiated by others.[83] Unfortunately, much of the evidence for rejection of allogeneic grafts in chambers has been achieved with mouse tumor tissues rather than grafts of normal tissue. A qualitative difference in the susceptibility of these two types of tissue to the cytotoxic action of antibody may explain the results.

Regarding the passive transfer of allograft sensitivity, a number of different grafted tissues have been studied. Transplantable mouse neoplasms fall into three categories[86,87]: those completely sensitive to the

27

in vitro and in vivo action of cytotoxic isoantibody; those completely resistant; and those of intermediate sensitivity. Such tumors can be shown in vitro to contain varying proportions of antibody-sensitive and antibody-resistant cells, the preponderance of one or the other type determining the way in which a given tumor can be classified. It seems apparent that, although passively transferred humoral antibody can prevent the take of a graft of dissociated tumor cells (that is, cause its rejection), it fails to do so if the graft has become a solid tumor of palpable size. Thus, the difference in effect with dissociated tumor cell grafts and solid tumors may be the relative ease of accessibility of antibody and complement to the former. Dissociated cell grafts of non-neoplastic lymphoid cells are also susceptible to passively transferred isoantibody. This has been well demonstrated by Harris et al.,[88] who noted the failure of function of antibody-producing rabbit lymphoid cells on transfer to other rabbits. This was interpreted as an allograft rejection reaction, and the immunity could be passively transferred with serum.[89] Recently, the immunity-transferring material has been characterized as antibody.[90] Siskind and Thomas[91] and Russell[92] have passively immunized newborn mice against grafts of adult mouse lymphoid cells, thus preventing runt disease.

Evidence for the vulnerability of solid orthotopic skin grafts to humoral antibody is less substantial. Extensive attempts by Billingham et al.[46,81] to transfer immunity to skin grafts in mice with serum failed. Reports of successful serum transfer of immunity invariably involve some artifact such as local injection of antibody around the graft[93] or attempts to increase local vascular permeability in the graft by selective injection of histamine.[76] Steinmuller's experiments are, however, of particular potential importance.[94] He showed that antiserum from BN rats, harvested at a time of maximum rejection of Lewis skin grafts, produced accelerated rejection of Lewis test grafts in normal BN animals. Established grafts in tolerant animals were not susceptible to the action of the antibody. Serum taken early after grafting and during rejection was much more effective than that harvested later when much higher levels of cytotoxic and hemagglutinating antibody were demonstrable. It should be noted that the majority of attempts to transfer immunity passively have involved the use of serum obtained after repeated immunizations rather than that harvested at a time of initial graft rejection. A possible qualitative difference between "early" and "late" antibody may exist. The suggestion that the latter may be 7S and the former 19S type gamma globulin, with their attendant differences in biologic properties, has been mentioned.

An interesting natural curiosity has long been cited as evidence against a significant role of antibody in the allograft rejection process. These observations spring from the fact that fetal lambs are born with essentially no circulating gamma globulin.[95] Silverstein has recently reviewed the development of immunologic competence in this animal.[96] Skin allografts applied to the fetus after the seventy-fifth day of gestation are rapidly rejected in a manner typical of adult sheep.[97] Since the fetal lamb has essentially no gamma globulin in its blood it has been possible to study the rejection of allografts in the presence of excess circulating rabbit antibody to sheep gamma and beta 2M globulins, without harm to the fetus.[95,98] In such a system antibodies formed by the fetus in its attempt to destroy the graft would be neutralized in the circulation and would thus be unavailable to participate in the rejection process. Despite the presence of persisting antibodies to sheep globulins the fetal lambs were found to reject allografts as rapidly, and as capably, as control fetuses uninjected with such antibodies. These data support the view that conventional circulating antibody is not an obligatory participant in the rejection of solid-tissue allografts.

Guiney, Austen and Russell[99] have recently added a carefully controlled study on the role of serum complement levels during allograft rejection. In rats these authors found no clear relation of total complement levels to first or second skin-graft rejection reactions. On the other hand, in the few human-kidney graft cases studied, they found that the titer of $C'_2{}^{hu}$ became distinctly depressed some three to five days after "threatened rejection" activity became manifest on other grounds (Fig. 5).

Failure to identify humoral antibody consistently as an effector in allograft rejection has led to much speculation about "cell-bound" antibody. It is known that certain immune serums contain a fraction of antibody that has a particular affinity for spleen cells.[100,101] This antibody firmly attaches to the cells and endows them with the capacity to interact specifically with antigen (Boyden's "cytophyllic antibody"). A similar phenomenon has been noted with normal lymphoid cells.[102] The term "cell-bound antibody" has been employed to describe the hypothetical modification of the sensitized cell in delayed sensitivity reactions and allograft sensitivity. Recent attempts to demonstrate specific mouse gamma globulin tightly bound to the surface of cells capable of effecting a specific allograft rejection have met with only limited success.[103] The recent experiments of Najarian and Feldman, however (described in the following section), appear to provide stronger evidence for such a phenomenon.

Subcellular Fractions Involved in Allograft Sensitivity

Recent years have seen extensive investigation in which it has been found that subcellular fractions may be involved in the transfer of allograft sensitivity. Attention has been paid to the possibility that viable sensitized cells capable of transferring allograft sensitivity may do so by passing on material, thought by some to be a special type of antibody[100,104] to the reticuloendothelial cells of the host, enabling them to act as if they themselves had been directly sensitized.

Lawrence and his co-workers have studied the problem extensively in man, in whom the situation has appeared to be unique. These workers have been able to extract a factor from human leukocytes derived from donors with delayed tuberculin-type hypersensitivity that will, on injection, transfer specific delayed hypersensitivity to a previously non-sensitized recipient. The altered reactivity produced is prompt, generalized and enduring. The agent involved in this transfer of immunologic information has been termed "transfer factor"[105] (Fig. 6). Delayed hypersensitivity to tuberculin, streptococcal antigen,[106] diphtheria toxoid[107] and coccidioidin[108] and allograft sensitivity has been transferred by such leukocytic extracts. Other investigators have achieved similar results.[109,110] The properties of transfer fac-

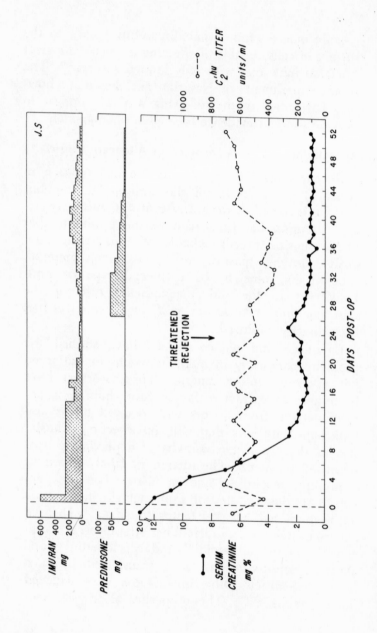

tor, described in detail by Lawrence,[105] include stability to repeated freezing and thawing (10 cycles),
to storage in the frozen state (five months), lysis
by distilled water, or to the action of desoxyribonu-
clease (DNase), ribonuclease (RNAse) and DNAse
and trypsin. Immunologically, the mechanism of action of transfer factor does *not* involve active sensitization (since the onset of sensitivity is too early) or
passive sensitization (because its duration is too
long). As little as 0.1 ml. provides for transfer of
systemic sensitivity. Apparently, a transfer factor (or
factors) seems to transfer immunologic information,

FIGURE 5. *Serum $C'_2{}^{hu}$ Complement Levels in Human Renal Allograft Rejection.*[99]

This figure illustrates the initial renal allograft rejection
crisis in a patient who is now 18 months post-transplantation
and doing well. Following renal allotransplantation the
serum creatinine fell from 20 mg.% to 1.2 mg.% over a
16-day period. Around day 24 the serum creatinine began to
rise, indicating the clinical onset of threatened rejection.
Prednisone, 60 mg. per day, was added on day 26 and the
rejection was averted. The $C'_2{}^{hu}$ titer, which had remained
at about 500 to 650 units per milliliter, fell to 350 to 400
units per milliliter about 6 days after the onset of clinical
rejection and did not return to preoperative levels until the
serum creatinine had been normal for 6 to 8 days. In a
second rejection crisis at about the 66th post-transplantation
day (not shown), the titer again fell to 200 $C'_2{}^{hu}$ units per
milliliter; on this occasion rejection was averted by holding
the Imuran dose at 120 mg. per day and increasing the
prednisone from 6 to 15 mg. per day. The $C'_2{}^{hu}$ levels have
remained normal for over a year since this second episode,
during which time the patient has shown no clinical signs of
rejection activity. The $C'_2{}^{hu}$ titer thus appears to fall 4 to 6
days after the onset of rejection and remains down until 6 to
10 days after the rejection has been clinically reversed.

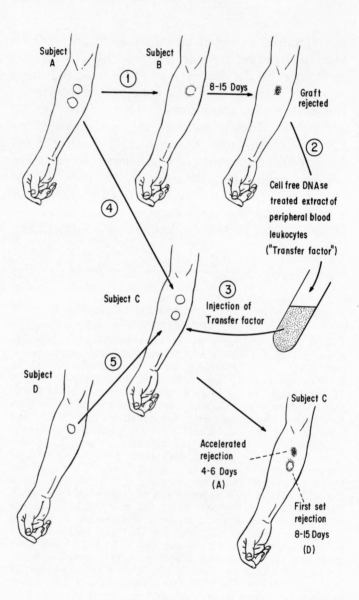

leading to self-replicating activity. A significant observation is the ability to transfer allograft sensitivity in man by local as well as systemic injection of leukocyte extracts from appropriately sensitized donors[47] (Fig. 7). The ability of such extracts to transfer allograft sensitivity in man is a striking departure from the requirement in animals for intact viable cells to achieve this effect. Brent, in collaboration with Lawrence,[49] failed to achieve the same result in the guinea pig. Turk,[111] however, reported transfer of sensitivity to picryl chloride in guinea pigs with a cell-free material. Subsequently, Powell et al.,[112] using a preparation very similar to Turk's, demonstrated that a skin reaction could be produced in guinea-pig skin-allograft donors with a cell-free substance extracted from the lymph nodes of recipients that had rejected the allograft. Recently, these authors[113] produced the accelerated rejection of guinea-pig allografts with this cell-free material, which they described as a partially purified transfer factor. The properties of this material were similar to those of the transfer factor described by Lawrence.

A potentially important, but as yet uncon-

FIGURE 6. *Transfer Factor in Man. Systemic sensitization.*[105]

Following sensitization of Subject B by a skin graft from Subject A, "transfer factor" (a DNAse-treated extract of leukocytes) is prepared from the peripheral blood of Subject B. When injected intramuscularly into a third person, Subject C, specific, long lasting, systemic sensitization to Subject A is conferred. This specific sensitivity is demonstrated by the accelerated rejection of a test skin graft from Subject A to Subject C as contrasted with the normal first-set rejection of a control skin graft from a neutral donor, Subject D.

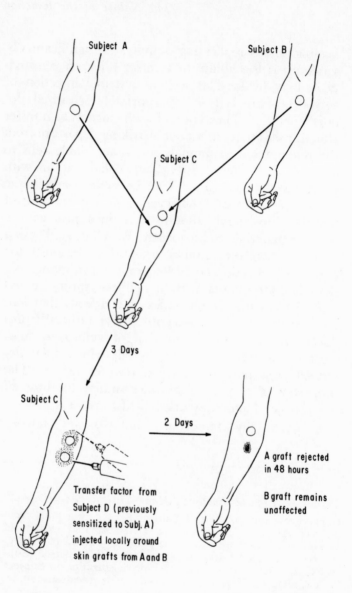

Subject A

Subject B

Subject C

3 Days

Subject C

2 Days

Transfer factor from
Subject D (previously
sensitized to Subj. A)
injected locally around
skin grafts from A and B

A graft rejected
in 48 hours

B graft remains
unaffected

firmed, series of experiments on the subcellular mechanisms involved in the transfer of allograft sensitivity in rodents has been reported by Najarian and Feldman.[57] These authors initially noted that tuberculin sensitivity was readily transferred in the guinea pig by means of sensitized leukocytes labeled with tritiated thymidine and that the labeled cells subsequently collected at the site of a tuberculin skin test. Tuberculin sensitivity in the guinea pig could not be transferred with sensitized cells enclosed in Millipore chambers. In mice passive transfer of allograft sensitivity was achieved with labeled sensitized cells, but in contrast to tuberculin sensitivity, few or no labeled cells were found at the graft site. Also, accelerated rejection of allografts in mice followed transfer of sensitized cells enclosed in Millipore chambers.[114] Subsequently, this was also found to be true in inbred guinea pigs, in which passive transfer of allograft sensitivity was achieved with sensitized cells, but few or no labeled cells were found at the graft site. Furthermore, sensitized cells enclosed in Millipore chambers transferred allograft immunity.[115] A similar finding had been reported by Kretschmer et al.[116] in rabbits. Contact sensitivity in the guinea pig gave results similar

---

FIGURE 7. *Transfer Factor in Man. Effect of local injection.*[105]

Subject C receives skin grafts from both Subject A and Subject B. Three days later transfer factor prepared from Subject D, previously sensitized only to Subject A by a prior skin graft, is injected locally around both the A and B skin grafts. Accelerated rejection of only the A skin graft then occurs. The B skin graft is rejected in normal, first-set style.

to tuberculin sensitivity. The authors concluded that, at least in the species investigated, tuberculin sensitivity and allograft immunity were mediated by different immunologic mechanisms. These authors subsequently extracted from lymph-node cells of sensitized donors a factor that, when given to normal animals, apparently accelerated the rejection of skin allografts. Preliminary analysis of this material suggested that it was a gamma globulin — that is, an antibody.[117] Obviously, an important step in the corroboration of this phenomenon would be an experiment in which tolerance is abolished by the transfer of sensitized cells in Millipore chambers. Thus far, attempts by Billingham et al.[118] and others to do this have failed.

There have been several investigations concerning the role of ribonucleic acid in transferring allograft sensitivity. The most significant is the experiment of Mannick and Egdahl[119] (Fig. 8). These investigators found that incubation of normal lymph-node cells from rabbit A with ribonucleic acid extracted

---

FIGURE 8. *The Experiment of Mannick and Egdahl.*[119]

Rabbit A first donates a sensitizing skin graft to Rabbit B. After the graft is rejected the regional lymph nodes are removed and an RNA extract is prepared from them. Dissociated normal lymph-node cells from Rabbit C are then incubated with this RNA extract for a few hours and the cells are washed and injected intradermally into Rabbit A. A positive "transfer reaction" (see Fig. 3,II) is achieved.

This experiment has been interpreted as an example of the transfer of specific immunologic sensitivity by the RNA extract from Rabbit B to the previously normal cells of Rabbit C.

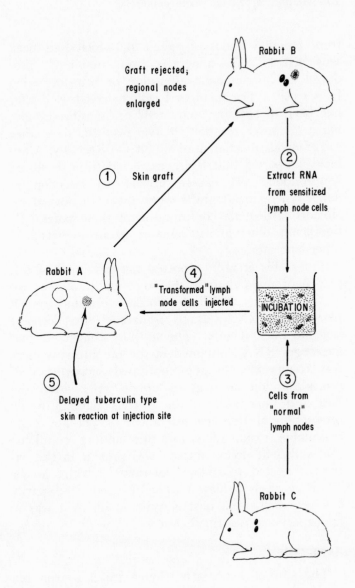

Rabbit B

Graft rejected;
regional nodes
enlarged

① Skin graft

② Extract RNA
from sensitized
lymph node cells

Rabbit A

④ "Transformed" lymph
node cells injected

INCUBATION

⑤

Delayed tuberculin type
skin reaction at injection site

③ Cells from
"normal"
lymph nodes

Rabbit C

from regional nodes of rabbit B, which had been sensitized by skin allografts from rabbit C, produced an immunologic alteration or transformation in A's cells. The incubated cells behaved as if they had been specifically "activated" or "sensitized," giving a "transfer reaction"[120] two or three days after intradermal injection into rabbit C. Recently, Mannick[121] reported that RNA, extracted from sensitized lymph-node cells, caused accelerated rejection of donor-type skin allografts when given to normal recipients. Adequate confirmation of these potentially significant observations remains to be achieved in other laboratories.

Trakatellis et al.[122] reported the induction of tolerance of male skin by the injection into newborn females of the C57BL/6J strain with microsomes, ribosomes or RNA extracts prepared from spleens of isogenic male donors. The authors concluded that messenger RNA, contained in the preparations used, was responsible for the continued biosynthesis of transplantation antigens of donor type within the host and thus initiated the process leading to the production of immune tolerance. A perhaps more reasonable explanation for this finding could be that sufficient donor antigen was present in the extracts injected to induce tolerance, which can be relatively easily achieved when the genetic disparity between donor and host is quite small, as it was in the experiment described above.

Xenografts

The use of xenografts (heterografts in the old terminology) for various purposes in surgery is a very old practice.[123] Its main attraction has always been the much more ready availability of tissues, a problem of growing urgency. Products derived from animal sources are regularly used, of course, in surgery for their mechanical properties. Such "static" grafts usually are soon absorbed, however, and catgut found an important place only when methods of reliably prolonging its residence before absorption were discovered by Lister, who first introduced treatment with chromic salts for this purpose.

The fundamental drawback to the use of living xenografts in clinical surgery is the fact that, in addition to potential differences in the whole array of individual-specific antigens that reflect the uniqueness of each individual, they differ from the recipient in the set of antigens reflecting species specificity. (The chemical nature of these additional antigens and their anatomic location on the cell are unknown.) The closer the species concerned, the less will be the immunologic reaction generated between them — in fact, the magnitude of these immunologic differences, in blood-group antigens particularly, have been used widely as evidence for such phylogenetic divergence.

In general, a xenograft among mammalian species is met with a more rapid and violent reaction than an allograft. Skin grafts among rodent species, for example, are scarcely able to become united to their beds and vascularized before the onward rush of the rejection reaction begins to take effect. Cellular infiltration is less obvious, and the vascular component of the reaction is more marked. Humoral antibodies directed against donor cells, including erythrocytes, are much more readily demonstrable than after allografts, and there have been suggestions that free antibody may be capable of destroying cells transferred to a xenogeneic environment without the participation of cells.[21]

Although the literature in this field is large, most reports deal with the behavior of xenogeneic grafts to immunologically privileged sites, particularly the anterior chamber of the eye or the hamster cheek pouch. Malignant tissues have often been used, thus introducing an additional variable, and no fully systematic information concerning the survival time of unprotected xenografts among common animals with the use of a standardized method is available.

In view of the greatly restricted survival enjoyed by most xenografts so far studied it is particularly noteworthy that, by the use of single doses of whole-body irradiation in the lethal range, stable, long-term chimeras have been established between rats and mice after infusions of xenogeneic bone-marrow suspensions.[124] Experiments in this class not only serve as an impressive example of the immunologic depressive effects of radiation but also give adequate grounds to discard any suspicion that grafts, at least between these two species, may not survive because of nonimmunologic factors, such as trophic or other metabolic differences, between the species.

Long-term immunologic tolerance has been produced between species of fowl, perhaps not widely disparate in genetic background,[125] but all attempts so far involving *in utero* or neonatal treatment of various species of small laboratory mammals have resulted in no more than the most modest evidence of prolonged survival[126] of later grafts of donor origin.

There have been several recent attempts to explore the therapeutic possibilities of xenogeneic organs from primates to patients. Although their effectiveness in the patient's behalf has been very limited, they have added some new information of interest that will be briefly set out in a following section.

3

ALTERATIONS IN RECIPIENT ACTIVITY

Lymphatic Ablation

The intimate involvement of the reticuloendothelial system in general, and the lymphoid system in particular, in the immune response has led to numerous attempts to ablate lymphoid tissue to alter the allograft response. Attempts at ablation have taken the form of surgical removal of lymphoid structures in the adult as well as a variety of ingenious maneuvers aimed at removal or destruction of individual circulating lymphocytes.

Surgical extirpation of lymphoid organs was the earliest method employed. Although splenectomy seems to decrease the humoral-antibody response to intravenously administered antigen in both man and the rat[127] no consistent prolongation of survival of skin allografts in rabbits after splenectomy was noted by Krohn.[128] It should be emphasized that the related phenomenon of enhancement (discussed at greater length in a later section of this chapter), mediated by circulating antibody, is depressed by prior splenectomy.[129] Excision of ipsilateral lymph nodes immediately before skin allografting failed to prolong graft survival significantly.[25,81] Excision of ipsilateral nodes and the sensitizing skin graft during its rejection (eleven days) failed to influence a subsequent second-set reaction. Recently, it has been reported that excision of both the graft and the regional lymph nodes at four days obviates the onset of immunity.[130] Taken together, these experiments show that the immune process engendered by a skin allograft resides in the regional nodes for a short time, but thereafter is systemically expressed, thus explaining the lack of success of experiments involving late nodal excision.

The rate of clearance of intravenously injected colloidal or particulate material is believed to be a measure of the phagocytic function of the reticuloendothelial system (RES). Administration of large quantities of such material frequently results in an altered physiologic state characterized by inability of the reticuloendothelial cell to function efficiently.[131,132] The terms "blockade" or "saturation" of the RES imply either that during this altered state the phagocytic cells are incapable of ingesting more material or that the rate at which additional particles can be ingested is markedly reduced.[133] Regarding humoral-antibody synthesis, there seems to be little doubt that depression of RES phagocytic activity by the administration of thorium oxide[134] and other materials[135] results in marked depression of antibody formation. Furthermore, stimulation of the RES phagocytic activity by Zymosan[136] and bacillus Calmette–Guérin (B.C.G.)[137] is associated with marked elevations in antibody response to particulate antigenic material. Whether RES blockade interferes with antibody synthesis by the RES directly[138] or prevents phagocytosis of antigen and its subsequent preparation before antibody formation by other cells[139] remains unsettled.

Concerning the allograft reaction, a definite prolongation of skin-graft survival even between animals differing at the H-2 locus was observed by Brent and Medawar utilizing trypan Blue as the blocking agent.[140] Recently, this result was reconfirmed by Medawar.[141] Others have failed to prolong allograft survival with RES blockade. Fisher and Fisher[142] have emphasized the fact that the allograft itself can cause enough stimulation of RES activity eventually to break through any blockade established. The discrepancies reported probably result from the variety of technics employed and agents used, particularly the timing of grafting, in relation to the degree of blockade achieved.

The intimate involvement of the small or medium-sized lymphocyte with the allograft reaction has led to attempts to achieve a specific deficiency of these cellular elements in the recipient animal. By far the most successful experiments have been those of Gowans and his colleagues. Chronic drainage of lymph from a thoracic-duct fistula in rats results in an immunologic deficiency that is due to the loss from the animal of small lymphocytes. The primary immune response of such animals to sheep erythrocytes and tetanus toxoid is severely depressed, although the secondary response is unaffected.[143-145] Subsequently, McGregor and Gowans[146] demonstrated that lymphocyte depletion by chronic drainage from a thoracic-duct fistula strikingly prolonged the survival of first-set allografts exchanged between members of a noninbred colony of rats. Grafts between closely related animals enjoyed markedly prolonged survival whereas grafts between distant combinations demonstrated only a modest prolongation in survival time. Drainage from a thoracic-duct fistula does not deprive an animal of all its small lymphocytes.[147] Apparently, a few small lymphocytes can initiate an allograft reaction against a graft containing "strong antigens" whereas a full supply of lymphocytes is required to mount a successful attack on allografts containing "weak antigens." The data of Woodruff and Anderson[148] is in agreement with this concept. It was further noted[146] that the effect of lymphocyte depletion was finite, and delay in application of allografts by eighteen days after closure of the fistula thus failed to prolong survival time. Likewise, lymphocyte depletion, begun at the time of rejection of a first-set graft, failed to prolong the survival of a second graft. The effect on second-set graft survival of lymphocyte depletion performed long after first-set rejection, when recollection of primary immunization could reside in circulating long lived effector cells,[118] has yet to be determined.

Recently, there has been renewed interest in the use of heterologous antilymphocyte serum specifically to depress or inhibit the immunologic capacity of the host. This concept is not without precedent, and early considerations may be found in a paper by Sacks et al.[149] Heterologous antiserum prepared against rat and guinea-pig lymphocytes causes lymphocytolysis in vitro and lymphopenia in vivo.[150,151] There are recorded attempts to maintain in vivo lymphopenia by chronic administration of antiserum, which resulted in an apparent state of refractoriness, in that absolute lymphocyte counts rose after ten to fourteen days in spite of repeated injections of antiserum.[152-154] This may have been due to the neutralizing effect of recipient antibody formed against the heterologous antiserum. Recently, Sacks et al.[149] reported maintenance of lymphopenia for twenty-one days in rats and questioned the existence of refractoriness during chronic administration. In our laboratory[155] lymphopenia has been maintained in certain strains of mice for eight weeks, whereas other strains seem to recover after four weeks. Others have described recovery from lymphopenia after a short time that can be followed by a second lymphopenic period on continued administration of antiserum.[156] The immunologic consequences of chronic administration of antilymphocyte serum can be profound. Waksman and his associates[157,158] found an inhibition of standard delayed sensitivity reactions in the rat but little effect on the allograft-rejection process. Subsequently, Woodruff and Anderson[159] demonstrated prolonged survival of rat-skin allografts with chronic administration of heterologous antilymphocyte serum. In mice[155] even short-term treatment with antilymphocyte serum results in a depression of capacity to synthesize humoral antibody to a salmonella antigen and a dramatic prolongation of skingraft survival in the face of an H-2 incompatibility (as long as fifty days). An interesting preliminary finding is that this effect does not correlate necessarily with the lymphopenia achieved, but rather there may be a specific alteration in the immunologic capacity of the lymphocyte, since lymphocytes from antiserum-treated animals do not produce runt disease when injected into neonatal recipients as readily

49

as equal numbers of lymphocytes from normal animals. Both chronic lymphocyte depletion via a thoracic-duct fistula and chronic administration of anti-lymphocyte serum have a certain inherent morbidity and mortality. Eventual application of these methods of lymphocyte suppression may be found either in the treatment of rejection crises in organ grafts or in its use temporarily to suppress or deplete the lymphoid population of the host as part of a program to induce a state of tolerance (as described below).

Several ingenious attempts at selective irradiation of lymphocytes have been reported. A relatively selective irradiation of lymphoid structures was achieved by the use of yttrium[90] chelated with di-ethylene triamine penta-acetic acid,[160] but the technic for continuous intravenous administration of this compound was rather cumbersome for prolonged use. On the other hand, Barnes[161] has found that insertion of a capsule, containing a beta-emitting source, into the right atrium of the dog permitted intensive irradiation of the circulating blood, with a subsequent depletion of lymphocytes in the peripheral blood and lymphoid organs and without significant side effects. The effect of the outcome of this relatively simple technic on the immunologic capacity of the altered animal remains to be tested.

Immunologic Tolerance and the Graft-versus-Host Reaction

Immunologic tolerance. The discovery of the phenomenon of *actively acquired immunologic tolerance* came about in the course of research into the transplantation of tissues. This term was used to describe a specific state of unresponsiveness to an antigen or antigens in adult life as a consequence of exposure to the antigen *in utero* or in the neonatal period. An elegant description of the background of this discovery can be found in Medawar's Nobel Lecture.[162]

In 1945 Owen[163] studied the immunogenetic consequences of vascular anastomoses between cattle twins *in utero*. Cattle twins are commonly synchorial, and Owen showed serologically that most cattle twins at birth are erythrocyte chimeras in that they possess their own erythrocytes and erythrocytes of the type belonging to the opposite twin. This chimeric state persists beyond the life-span of the erythrocyte, indicating that erythropoietic cells must have been exchanged in fetal life and have continued subsequently to produce erythrocytes of characteristic serologic type.[164,165] Erythrocyte chimerism appears to be rare in animals other than cattle, but it has been demonstrated in the lamb[166] and in man on at least three occasions.[167-169]

A few years later Burnet and Fenner[170,171] emphasized the wide significance of Owen's observation in proposing a general theory of the immune response that predicted the phenomenon of tolerance among its consequences. To explain failure of the adult to react immunologically to its own tissues, either in their normal state or as damaged body constituents, these authors suggested that body cells possess some type of "self-marker" component and that the capacity to recognize this self-pattern develops during embryonic or early postnatal life. They thus predicted that exposure to antigen in embryonic life would cause *that* antigen to be recognized as "self" in later life in that no immune response would be made to it.

It soon became clear that erythrocyte chimerism

was but one manifestation of tolerance in dizygotic cattle twins resulting from admixture of placental circulations. Medawar and his colleagues showed that most dizygotic cattle twins would accept skin grafts from each other, regardless of differences in sex or color, and that this mutual tolerance was specific since skin transplanted from third parties was quickly rejected.[172,173] The causal connection between Owen's discovery and this observation was appreciated, and the stage was set to provide for the acceptance by adult animals of tissue allografts by reproducing in the laboratory the state of affairs that had been observed as a natural accident in twin cattle.

The initial and subsequent experiments by Billingham, Brent and Medawar[174,175] to produce actively acquired tolerance involved injection of mouse embryos of the CBA strain *in utero* through the anterior abdominal wall with a suspension of living spleen cells of the A strain[174] (Fig. 9). When the CBA recipients had grown to adulthood they were regularly found to accept A-strain skin grafts. The tolerance so induced was specific since CBA mice tolerant of A-strain tissues easily rejected allografts from the unrelated AU strain. At about the same time Hašek[176,177] reproduced Owen's phenomenon in chickens by the ingenious method of making a deliberate synchorial parabiosis of avian embryos via the chorioallantoic membrane in the shell. At hatching the parabionts were separated, and from then on they were incapable of making antibodies to each other's red cells, or of rejecting grafts of each other's skin.[178] It was subsequently demonstrated that *in utero* injection was not necessary and

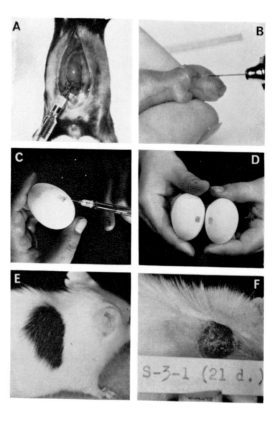

that mice injected intravenously within a few days of birth could be rendered tolerant. Injections made thereafter were progressively less effective.[179] The intravenous route was obligatory for consistent results although some animals became tolerant when injected intraperitoneally; subcutaneous injection was totally ineffective. The next important finding was that the tolerant state could be abolished by injection of the tolerant animal with lymphoid cells from normal adult members of the same strain.[180] More rap-

---

FIGURE 9. *Technics of Induction and Abolition of Immunologic Tolerance.*

Various means of delivering allogeneic cells to immature recipients have been used.

A. The *in utero* injection of a suspension of living dissociated allogeneic spleen cells directly into the mouse fetus at 10 to 12 days of gestation by the original method of Billingham, Brent and Medawar.[174]

B. The intravenous injection of a spleen-cell suspension into the facial vein of a neonatal mouse by the technic of Billingham and Brent.[179]

C. Direct injection of cell suspension into exposed chorioallantoic vessel of fertilized chick egg at about 11 days of incubation.

D. Preparation of artificial synchorial chick twins by a technic of producing parabiosis of eggs in which the chorionic vessels of each become confluent through adjacent windows cut at appropriate locations in their shells.[176]

E. A fully tolerant A-strain mouse bearing a healthy CBA skin graft for more than 100 days as a consequence of having received an intravenous injection of CBA spleen cells within 12 hours of birth. The CBA skin graft was placed at 6 weeks of age.

F. An adult A-strain mouse, previously fully tolerant of CBA skin, has rejected its CBA skin graft 21 days after receiving an intraperitoneal injection of spleen cells from another adult A-strain mouse which had recently rejected a CBA skin allograft.

id and dramatic abolition of tolerance is possible
with the use of cells from such a donor that had
previously rejected a graft derived from the tolerance-
inducing strain (Fig. 10). This critical observation led
Medawar and his colleagues to define tolerance as
the outcome of "a specific central failure of the
mechanism of immunological response brought about
by exposure of animals to antigenic stimuli before
maturation of the faculty of immunological response."

It was soon shown that tolerant mice, when carefully tested, were chimeras so far as their lymphoid-
cell populations were concerned.[181] Furthermore,
tolerance, so induced, was frequently permanent.
This was in sharp contrast to the transient nature
of the tolerance observed by a number of investigators when nonliving, nonreplicating antigens such
as proteins were injected into neonatal animals for

FIGURE 10. *Induction and Abolition of Actively Acquired
Immunologic Tolerance in the Mouse.*

A suspension of dissociated lymphoid cells is prepared from
an adult CBA donor. This cell suspension is injected intravenously into a neonatal A-strain recipient which is then permitted to grow normally. A later CBA-strain skin graft to
the adult A-strain animal survives indefinitely, and the
lymphoid structures and peripheral blood of this A-strain animal can be demonstrated to contain both CBA and A cells,
i.e. it is a "chimera."

The tolerated skin graft and chimeric state may be abolished by the injection of A-strain lymphoid cells. If these
cells originate from normal A-strain donors, the tolerated
skin graft is rejected slowly in about one month (*a*). If the
A-strain donor has previously rejected a CBA skin allograft,
the "adoptive immunity" is reflected by a much more rapid
rejection of the test CBA skin graft (*b*).

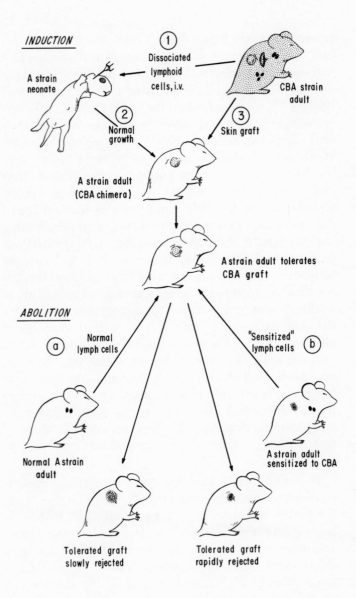

INDUCTION

① Dissociated lymphoid cells, i.v.

A strain neonate   CBA strain adult

② Normal growth

③ Skin graft

A strain adult (CBA chimera)

A strain adult tolerates CBA graft

ABOLITION

Ⓐ Normal lymph cells

Ⓑ "Sensitized" lymph cells

Normal A strain adult

A strain adult sensitized to CBA

Tolerated graft slowly rejected

Tolerated graft rapidly rejected

varying periods from birth.[182-184] Both the duration and the degree of reduction of antibody formation seemed to depend upon the amount of antigen initially injected. The experiments of Smith and Bridges[182] suggested that the duration of the tolerant state depended upon persistence of the antigen. Rabbits injected with bovine serum albumin at birth and challenged several months later were less likely to react with antibody formation if they had already been challenged one to four times. Shortly thereafter, Mitchison clearly demonstrated that tolerance of fowl erythrocytes, a nonreplicating antigen, could only be maintained by repeated injection of allogeneic erythrocytes, and the state of tolerance could easily be abolished at any time if erythrocyte injections were stopped. The point of abolition was reached two to twenty-five days after the last allogeneic erythrocyte left the recipient bloodstream.[185] These conclusive experiments, when coupled with the observation of chimerism in tolerant mice, led Medawar to redefine tolerance as follows: "if an animal is exposed to antigen before it has developed the capacity to react against it, then the development of that capacity is delayed and, in the continued presence of antigen, can be indefinitely postponed."[186]

It is quite clear that the more distant the genetic relation between the donor and the immature host, the more difficult it will be to induce tolerance. Such a situation is represented in mice when donor and recipient differ by the strong H-2 histocompatibility locus. When this genetic barrier is involved, a large inoculum of cells is required, the intravenous route of injection is almost obligatory, and, most important, the tolerance-responsive period extends for only a short time after birth. On the other hand, when the genetic, and therefore antigenic, disparity involved is relatively weak, such stringent requirements disappear. Billingham and Silvers found that induction of tolerance in C57 female mice to the weak antigens present in C57 male skin grafts was easily achieved by the injection of cells by any route and that the tolerance-responsive period extended seventeen days after birth. It is now well documented that tolerance of tissue allografts can be induced in adult mice of certain strains, differing by weak histocompatibility loci, by the simple maneuver of parabiotic union between allogeneic individuals[187-189] or either by the intravenous administration of a single large dose of viable splenic cells[190,191] or by repeated injections of splenic cells intravenously or intraperitoneally.[192] An important observation is that when donor and host differ at the weak H-3 histocompatibility locus, adult mice can be either sensitized or rendered unresponsive to a subsequent skin graft, depending on the number of lymphoid cells injected.[193] Furthermore, adult mice could be rendered unresponsive, even when donor and recipient strains differed at the H-2 locus, if they were injected intravenously, and over a long time, with large numbers of splenic cells (1.5 $\times$ 10^9 in seven weeks).[192]

The interpretation of the original experiments was that the phenomenon of tolerance depended upon a qualitative difference in reactivity of the embryo or neonate to antigen, and that the individual's reactivity underwent a striking inversion shortly after birth in most species. The induction of tolerance in adult animals, described above, provoked extensive investigation. Brent and Gowland explored the nature of the difference in immunologic reactivity between neonatal and adult animals by making a systematic study of the relation between antigen dose and age of recipient in the induction of tolerance to tissue allografts differing at the H-2 histocompatibility locus.[194-196] By utilizing a weight-adjusted dose of lymphoid cells as the tolerance-conferring inoculum to take into account the increase in size and lymphoid mass of the recipient, they extended the tolerance-responsive period after birth for only approximately a week. However, a single injection of ten times the weight-adjusted dose for twelve-day-old animals failed to induce tolerance, and the authors concluded that neonatally induced tolerance was not simply a scaled-down version of the tolerance induced in adults by massive injections of antigen. Michie and Howard showed that whereas large doses of allogeneic spleen cells injected neonatally did indeed produce *tolerance,* very small doses induced *sensitivity,* detected by an ingenious assay based on the protective effect of the inoculum against a subsequent graft-versus-host reaction.[197-199] Further evidence for the presence of immunologically competent cells in newborn mice was uncovered by Brent and Gowland,[200] who noted that the prior injection of a small dose of splenic cells decreased, to some extent, the tolerance induced by a subsequent, large, weight-adjusted dose of such cells. These authors concluded that immunologically competent cells are present in the neonate, but in much smaller numbers than in later life. It should be emphasized that evidence also exists that fetal mammals of other species can initiate immunologic responses.[95,201,202] A further similar important observation with a different immune system was that of Siskind.[203] He noted that small doses of pneumococcal polysaccharide, injected neonatally, protected against subsequent exposure to living pneumococci, but large doses induced susceptibility.

Brent and Gowland also studied the induction of tolerance in adults with splenic cells. Beginning thirteen days after birth, A-strain mice were injected repeatedly with large doses of $(CBAxA)F_1$ hybrid spleen cells, administered intravenously every third or fourth day. Test skin allografts from hybrid donors were placed on the day of the last injection.[194] Animals injected for two weeks showed a modest degree of tolerance of subsequent skin grafts, but those injected for longer periods were highly tolerant. This evidence suggested that the establishment of tolerance was progressive and that before unresponsiveness was fully established a transient period of sensitization occurred (Fig. 11). Further, the authors found that mice rendered tolerant by this regimen were cellular chimeras and that the tolerance could be broken by transfer of normal or presensitized adult lymph-node cells from the host strain. They concluded that tolerance induced in adult animals was indistinguishable from that achieved by fetal or neonatal injection. Finally, it was found to be possible to induce tolerance in neonatal mice by repeated injection of cell doses (0.5 $\times$ 10^6 cells) too small to have produced tolerance if given only once. This result essentially mimicked the results of experiments with thirteen-day-old mice,

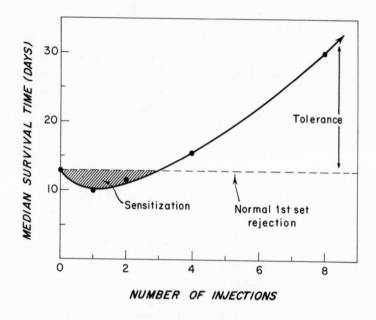

FIGURE 11. *The Experiment of Brent and Gowland.*[194] *Induction of tolerance in adults with repeated injection of spleen cells.*

In this experiment A-strain mice 13 days old were injected repeatedly every 3 or 4 days with large doses of (CBAxA)F₁ spleen cells. After various numbers of injections, groups of mice received test skin allografts from the hybrid strain. The resulting median survival times are plotted against the number of injections received prior to allografting. It can be seen that a small number of injections sensitized the animals to the test allografts. With a larger number of injections, animals were not sensitized but had slight prolongation of survival. With still larger numbers of injections, animals showed marked prolongation of survival and many were highly tolerant of the test allografts.

This experiment emphasized that establishment of tolerance is a progressive phenomenon which can be preceded by a transient period of sensitization. The same curve is obtained if antigen in a cell-free form is utilized in place of living cells.[493]

and added further weight to the authors' contention that the difference between tolerance induction in newborn and adult mice is a quantitative one.

Although the quantitative features of the induction of tolerance in both neonatal and adult animals are becoming apparent, no final statement as yet can be made concerning the cellular nature of tolerance. Michie and Howard[204] believe that their results argue against a "stem-cell theory" of tolerance postulating that antigen sensitizes mature cells and induces tolerance in immature stem cells. Rather, these authors maintain that cells are equally susceptible to an appropriate paralyzing dose of excess antigen at any stage of life. Special qualities are not demanded of stem cells.

The concept that the induction of tolerance, particularly in adult animals, rests at least to some degree on the quantitative relation between the amount of antigen presented and the immunologic reactivity of the host has provided impetus for a number of experiments in which the host's lymphoid population is depleted or reduced in some way prior to the introduction of antigen. Lymphoid depletion has been accomplished by various drugs or irradiation, and antigen has been used in the form of living cells or cell-free extracts. Uphoff[205,206] induced tolerance in mice of subsequent skin and tumor grafts by pretreatment of the host with A-methopterin (Methotrexate) together with splenic and thymus cells of appropriate origin. To achieve this, it was necessary to administer drugs and cells at high levels for considerable periods. In similar experiments injections of 6-mercaptopurine alone caused only a modest prolongation of skin allografts in mice across a non-H-2 barrier. When combined with injections of donor spleen cells, however, this treatment resulted in clear-cut tolerance of skin grafts. Attempts to demonstrate chimerism in such situations have frequently been inconclusive,[207] but chimerism has been documented when the genetic disparity has been particularly weak.[208] On the other hand, the use of radiation before treatment with allogeneic cells has produced tolerance across the H-2 barrier, and the existence of chimerism in this situation has been elegantly documented.[209] A previous attempt to apply this principle to the problem of renal allograft rejection had not been successful.[210] These experiments involved the treatment of dogs with 6-mercaptopurine in addition to various cellular antigens (lymphoid cells, buffy coat, splenic homogenate) before renal transplantation.

It may not be necessary to use living cells as a source of antigen to induce tolerance of allografted tissues. Indeed, the fear of an attendant graft-versus-host reaction (discussed below) adds an undesirable element to use of living cells. Some progress has already been made. Linder[211] and Billingham and Silvers[212] induced tolerance of weak histocompatibility antigens by repeated injections of cell-free extracts of donor tissues. Medawar[141] found that a single intravenous injection of cell-free antigenic material in its crude soluble form could prolong the life of subsequent skin allografts. The effect was achieved in face of strong histocompatibility antigens as well as weaker ones. Furthermore, the prolongation achieved was not due to enhancement. Pretreatment of the animals with drugs or irradiation augmented this prolongation of survival.

Subsequently, Martinez et al.[213] produced tolerance, where both strong and weak antigenic combinations were concerned, in adult animals by repeated injections of splenic-cell extracts over long periods. Survival of test grafts for periods of up to three months was achieved. The tolerant state so induced was shown not to involve chimerism. These experiments lead to the important conclusion that tolerance can be induced by transplantation antigens in a cell-free form. Once the state of tolerance is induced, slow release of antigen from the graft itself may be sufficient to maintain it. This concept has particular appeal, as suggested by Medawar, where large organ grafts such as kidneys are directly connected to the host blood stream.[141]

The graft-versus-host reaction. The immunologic attack of a grafted cell population against the host has been studied intensively. Simonsen's exhaustive and scholarly treatment of the subject includes the details.[214] In 1957 Simonsen[215] reported that adult splenic cells, when injected into newborn or embryo chickens and mice, produced a disease that could only be interpreted as an outcome of an immunologic response by the grafted cells against the host. At the same time Billingham and Brent[216] found, in attempts to induce tolerance in newborn mice, that in certain strain combinations, all the injected animals died as a result of the subsequent development of a peculiar wasting disease. They concluded that a graft-versus-host reaction was the likely explanation of this pathologic condition, which they named *runt disease.* Graft-versus-host reactions (hereafter referred to as GVH reactions) result when the recipient of a graft of immunologically competent cells is incapable of rejecting the graft. This situation occurs in very young individuals (embryo and new-born recipients). It also occurs in grafting from a homozygous (AA) donor to a host that is the F_1 hybrid between the donor strain and a dissimilar homozygote (BB). Thus a graft A→AB represents a situation in which the hybrid host cannot reject the graft by immunologic means, even though the host may be entirely capable immunologically. This is so because the graft does not possess any antigens that are foreign to the host. On the other hand, the graft can react against the host, since the latter contains foreign antigens derived from the BB parent of the hybrid.

Although GVH reactions have been demonstrated in many species, the mouse is the classic animal for the production of runt disease.[216,217] In the "worst"-strain combinations mice usually grow normally for the first week, but thereafter growth ceases and there is a subsequent loss of weight associated with severe diarrhea, alopecia, dermatitis and eventual death (see Fig. 16a,b). Some succumb quickly, but in others the disease takes a chronic form and the victims linger for months before death. Pathologically runted animals have characteristic splenomegaly and hepatomegaly, but atrophy of the lymph nodes, thymus and Peyer's patches. Histologically, the changes in the lymphoid follicles can be observed to go through two phases. The first change is a displacement of the normal lymphocytes and concomitant replacement by proliferation of other cell types, including many that are pyroninophilic and probably belong to the plasma-cell series. If the animal lives long enough atrophy and fibrosis of lymphoid tissue follow. Splenomegaly

is an easily detectable sign of the first proliferative
phase, which involves the whole lymphoid system.
The origin of the pyroninophilic cells has received
considerable attention. The elegant experiments of
Gowans et al.[218] clearly show that at least some represent transformed cells of the original inoculum.
On the other hand, at the peak of splenomegaly in
the mouse, when there is evidence that almost all the
cells may be of host origin, many are still pyroninophilic. Thus, splenomegaly can be attributed, in
large measure, to host reactivity.

An outcome of the studies on the pathology of
GVH reactions has been the incorporation of the
various pathologic effects into assay systems for determining the strength of the GVH reaction. Russell[219] utilized the growth retardation of runt disease
in his weight-gain assay. Such an assay has ad-
vantages over the use of mortality rates alone, since
the disease is not always lethal.[220] Simonsen has designed a particularly sensitive assay, which depends
upon the regular splenomegaly occurring at a certain stage of the disease. This is expressed as a
ratio of spleen to body weight in the affected animal.[215,221] A modification of this assay is the "discriminant spleen assay," which makes it possible, in
a mixture of immunologically competent cells of
different origin, to measure the activity of one component only by an appropriate selection of recipients.[222] Such an assay is particularly useful in the
analysis of GVH reactions in radiation chimeras.

The GVH reaction and concomitant runt disease can be prevented in mice by various immunologic interventions designed to assist the newborn
recipient to reject (or possibly inactivate) the graft

of adult lymphoid cells (Fig. 12). Isogeneic adult splenic cells injected shortly after the foreign splenic cells decrease the mortality from later runt disease,[91,223] and adult cells from animals preimmunized to the donor strain have an even better protective

FIGURE 12. *Runt Disease and Its Modification in Mice.*[92]

C57BL/6 mice which receive a neonatal intravenous injection of 5,000,000 or more dissociated adult DBA/1 spleen cells develop runt disease which is reflected in failure to gain weight beyond about the first week of life.

Top left. The weight gain curve of normal, untreated C57BL/6 neonatal mice *(solid points)* is compared with that of mice which have received an intravenous injection of 10,000,000 DBA/1 spleen cells *(open points).* The injected animals soon show symptoms of runt disease and are all dead by 3 weeks after birth.

Top right. The effect of the neonatal DBA/1 spleen cell inoculum is ameliorated by a subsequent injection *(arrow)* of adult C57BL/6 spleen cells. If these are derived from normal animals *(X points),* the young animals' recovery is slow. If the second injection makes use of cells from adult C57BL/6 mice which have previously *rejected* DBA/1 skin grafts, its effect is much more prompt, resulting in normal weight gain of the neonatal animals *(solid points).* Control runts without a second injection succumb as usual *(open points).*

Bottom left. The onset of runt disease in C57BL/6 neonatal mice which have received a neonatal injection of DBA/1 spleen cells is prevented by a series of three intraperitoneal injections of a cytotoxic antiserum *(arrows)* directed against DBA/1 antigens. Prompt destruction of the runt-producing DBA/1 cells thus allows normal development.

Bottom right. The otherwise inevitable onset of runt disease in DBA/1-cell-injected C57BL/6 newborns is obviated by three injections of Methotrexate (A-methopterin), 0.37 mg./Kg. *(arrows).* The resultant healthy adult C57BL/6 mice are fully and specifically tolerant of DBA/1 skin grafts, indicating persistence of cell descendants of the original inoculum.

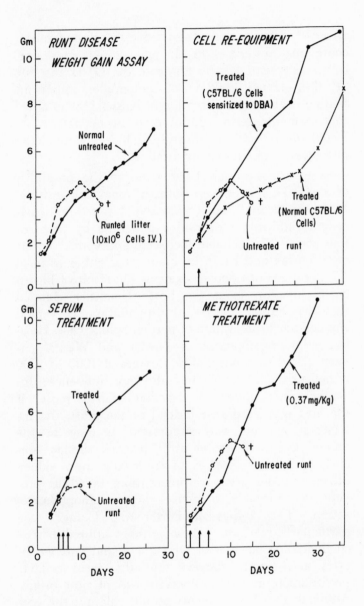

effect.[219] Furthermore, the passive transfer of serum containing antibodies to antigens present in donor-strain cells, can largely abrogate the GVH reaction by the grafted cells.[223] A potentially important finding is also the observation of Russell,[92] who noted that A-methopterin administered to neonatally injected mice could significantly reduce the incidence and severity of subsequent runting.

Some attention has been given to the possibility of a GVH reaction in human renal allografting. Both Dempster[224] and Simonsen[225] noted an early cellular infiltration of canine allografts by three or four days. The cellular foci were widespread in the renal cortex and could be interpreted either as local proliferations of donor cells or as the result of blood-borne invasion from the host. Dempster claimed that irradiation before transplantation prevented this cellular proliferation of pyroninophilic cells. However, the investigations of Fowler and West[226] entirely failed to confirm this. Dosages of 1000 to 1500 r delivered to the kidney did not influence this characteristic interstitial reaction. Furthermore, if the host was irradiated instead of the graft, the interstitial reaction was suppressed as long as the animal lived. Hume et al.[227] reached similar conclusions in that 3000 r, given locally to a kidney fifteen minutes after transplantation, failed to prevent, or noticeably to reduce, the pyroninophilic reaction. The studies of Porter and Calne[228] are particularly relevant. These authors utilized tritiated thymidine labeling of both donor and host leukocytes and clearly showed that the early cellular proliferation in renal allografts was of host origin. Although these experiments do not rule out the possibility that the mesenchyme of a renal allograft contributes to the interstitial pyroninophilic reaction, they form a consistent body of evidence to the contrary.

Enhancement

Immunologic enhancement may be defined as the successful establishment, or delayed rejection, of an allograft as a consequence of the presence of specific antiserum in the host.[229] The existence of antigraft antibody as the effective agent in enhancement distinguishes this phenomenon from other types of immune unresponsiveness. The basic conditions for inducing enhancement have been worked out extensively in inbred mice and have been reviewed in detail.[230] Although this phenomenon was discovered in experiments involving tumor transplantation and has since been studied extensively with similar systems, it should be emphasized that enhancement extends likewise to normal tissues although it may often be less easy to demonstrate where they are used.[140] Progressive growth, by enhancement, of tumor grafts in certain strains in which they normally would be rejected may follow active immunization of the host with killed (lyophilized) tumor tissue or normal tissue of the strain to which the tumor is indigenous (Fig. 13). Tissues vary in their enhancing activity, certain tumors (particularly sarcoma I), spleen and parotid gland being the best sources.[231] Enhancement also follows passive immunization of the host with isoantiserum or heteroantiserum directed against the tumor graft. (Fig. 14).

Induction of enhancement is more reliable by pas-

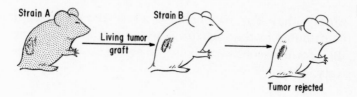

Strain A
Living tumor graft →
Strain B →
Tumor rejected

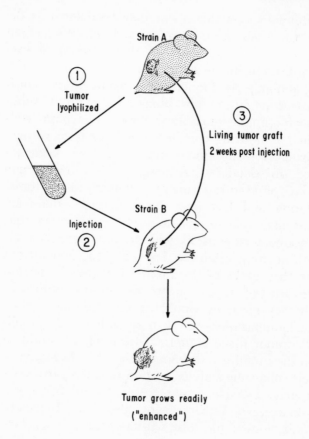

Strain A

① Tumor lyophilized

③ Living tumor graft 2 weeks post injection

② Injection →

Strain B →

Tumor grows readily ("enhanced")

sive immunization with potent antiserum than by direct stimulation by active immunization; this is apparently due to qualitative and quantitative differences among various inbred strains to immunologic stimuli. When lyophilized tissues are used to actively establish enhancement, allograft sensitivity, rather than enhancement, may occur if the dose of lyophilized tissue[232] and the interval to grafting[233] are carefully adjusted. In general, however, if killed tissue is the initial immunizing material, enhancement, rather than rejection, occurs with a subsequent tumor inoculum. Apparently, killed tissue does not provoke an efficient cellular response (presumably the major operant in graft rejection) but does provoke a good humoral response, the essential factor in enhancement. Both allograft sensitivity and enhancement can be demonstrated in the actively immunized animal.[234-236] If a live tumor allograft is transferred initially and subsequently rejected, a second graft of the same tumor, inoculated between five and fourteen days after the first graft, will exhibit accelerated rejection. As the interval between first- and second-set grafting is increased, enhancement of the second grafts may occur. This can be

---

FIGURE 13. *Active Enhancement.*

Upper. A tumor indigenous to one strain of mouse (strain A) is ordinarily rejected as usual for allografts of living cells when transferred to a second strain (strain B).

Lower. The indigenous tumor arising in strain A is removed and freeze-dried (lyophilized). This preparation is then injected into the recipient mouse of strain B. Two weeks later a transplant of living tumor is performed. This tumor then grows vigorously and is said to be "enhanced."

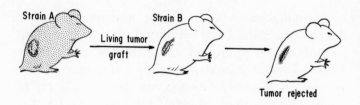

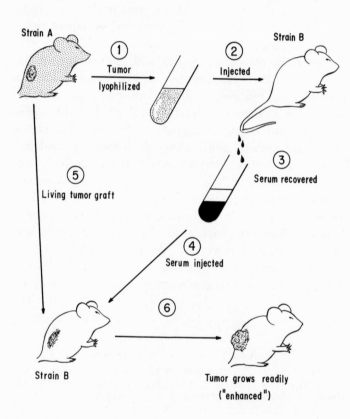

interpreted as a waning of allograft resistance and the appearance and persistence of enhancing antibody. Immunologic enhancement is more easily demonstrated with certain classes of tumors than others,[237,238] the ease of induction of enhancement bearing an inverse relation to the extent to which a given tumor is sensitive to the cytotoxic action of isoantibody. On the other hand, regardless of the type of tumor grafted, the relative doses of tumor cells and antiserum may be critical in determining whether enhancement or graft destruction will ensue.[87,239,240]

Although it is generally agreed that the contact of graft and antigraft antibody is necessary for enhancement the actual mechanism involved is unknown. The theories proposed have included "afferent" blockade of the immune response,[241,242] "efferent" blockade,[140] alteration of the enhanced graft[230,235,236] and possible "immunoselection" of graft cells, through the intercession of serum antibody in some way, which are resistant to the host

---

FIGURE 14. *Passive Enhancement.*

Upper. A tumor indigenous to one strain of mouse (strain A) is ordinarily rejected as usual for allografts of living cells when transferred to a second strain (strain B).

Lower. The indigenous tumor arising in strain A is removed and freeze-dried (lyophilized). This preparation is then injected into the recipient mouse of strain B. Two weeks later the recipient mouse is bled and the serum recovered. This serum is then injected into a second strain B animal. The serum recipient is then grafted with a living tumor allograft. This graft is not rejected but grows progressively, i.e. is "enhanced."

immune responses. Against the blockade hypotheses is the evidence that enhancement of a tumor allograft can occur during a time when an allograft reaction is occurring against a prior skin graft of the same genetic makeup[235,243] and that the enhanced graft can impart allograft sensitivity to a subsequent graft.[229,234] Regarding graft alteration, enhanced tumors are specifically vulnerable to second-set immunity generated by unenhanced tumors; apparently, their antigens are qualitatively unchanged, although the possibility of reduced antigenic content remains.[229] Similar results might occur because of other than antigenic alterations in such cells, as pointed out by Gorer.[237] Another pertinent observation is that the antiserum given one week after inoculation of a tumor graft may cause enhancement of the graft, even though it has undergone initial regression. Furthermore, the same antiserum does not protect a second graft inoculated one week after the first from a second-set reaction induced by the first graft. Thus, a general depression of the immune response cannot be the sole explanation although it is known that the intensity and speed of development of the second-set response may be somewhat lessened in a passively conditioned animal.[234] Finally, a simple "walling-off" action of antibody is doubtful, in view of the very small amount of antibody required for enhancement.[237] Rather, a qualitative change in the reaction of unsensitized host cells with antigen and antibody has been postulated by Kaliss.[229]

He has proposed a broad schema of the mechanism of enhancement based on three general observations. Gorer's studies of tumor allograft rejection showed that tumor growth was associated with rapid vascularization and subsequent histiocytic proliferation. Rejection was intimately related to violent histiocytic activity.[86] In enhanced mice histiocytic proliferation did not appear, but rather a rapid mitosis of tumor cells occurred, believed by Gorer to be an actual stimulation by antibody.[244] The second observation was the demonstration that interaction between antibody and sensitized cells can be either antagonistic or synergistic, depending upon the relative doses used and the route of administration.[238,239,245] Synergy was demonstrated by marked inhibition of subcutaneous tumor growth in mice receiving an intraperitoneal injection of a "subeffective dose" of sensitized lymph-node cells combined with antiserum, the latter at a level usually producing enhancement. With a tumor inoculated intraperitoneally, antiserum antagonized the activity of an otherwise inhibitory dose of sensitized cells. Amos[246] has suggested that the actual process of graft destruction may be cell damage by enzymes liberated by sensitized host cells in close contact with cells of the graft. Release of enzymes is attendant upon lysis of host cells brought about by antigen-antibody interactions at the cell surface. Resultant destruction of graft cells releases more antigen to react with sensitized host cells, and a "chain reaction" of mutual destruction is set in motion. According to Kaliss's schema, the presence of a high level of antibody would on the one hand effect enhancement of a first graft ("antagonism") and on the other implement the destruction of a second graft ("synergism"). "Synergy" between antiserum and sensitized cells would account for destruction of a second graft despite a reduced number of sensitized cells in the enhanced mouse.[247] "Antagonism" would permit enhancement of a single graft since excess antiserum would decrease antigen transfer from graft to host cells and hence would prevent their lysis and the release of destructive enzymes. If, added to this, actual stimulation of the graft occurred on contact with excess antiserum, progressive growth of the tumor graft beyond mere delay in regression would be assured.

Although the complex process of enhancement is not yet fully understood, it must not be forgotten as a possible explanation where anomalous survival of allografts has occurred. Halasz and Orloff[248,249] recognized this in their experiments in which prior subcutaneous injections of donor blood significantly prolonged canine renal allografts. An interesting finding was the rather consistent effectiveness of this treatment, in view of the great variability of similar treatments in other species.

Radiation and Radiation Chimerism

Total-body irradiation may have a powerful effect on immunologic responses. When nonreproducing antigens are given as a primary antigenic challenge within forty-eight hours of irradiation maximum inhibition of antibody formation is observed.[250,251] This result suggests that the preinduction phase of antibody evocation is highly radiosensitive. Taliaferro[251] also found that so long as the capacity to synthesize antibody had been initiated, irradiation had little effect on subsequent antibody production. The effect of radiation on the response to a secondary antigenic stimulus varies with the species used and the nature of the antigen. The effect of radiation on the anamnestic response of rabbits to sheep erythrocytes is about the same as its effect on the primary response. On the other hand, in mice the depressive effect on the response to a secondary antigenic stimulus is considerably less pronounced than on that to a primary one.[252] The influence of radiation on either the primary or the secondary response seems to be roughly proportional to the radiation dose.[253]

Similarly, it has been shown that the allograft-rejection reaction can be modified by total-body irradiation. Dempster et al.[254] first demonstrated that survival of skin allografts on rabbits was prolonged by prior irradiation. Kent,[255] also working with rabbits, obtained a similar result and showed furthur that the greater the dose of irradiation (up to 700 r), the longer skin allografts survived. Doses in excess of 700 r did not further increase the survival time. Considerable variation in the effect of irradiation on the allograft response occurs not only because of varying genetic differences between animals but also probably because of variations in the time and rate at which antigens are released from different types of grafts.

The effect of irradiation on transplantation *antigens* has received little attention. McKhann[256] recently studied the effect of graded doses of x-rays, delivered in vitro, on the immunizing capacity of lymphoid and tumor cells. He found that when strong histocompatibility factors, associated with the H-2 locus, were involved, irradiated cells induced immunity after as much as 12,800 r. However, when only weaker histocompatibility factors were involved, similar numbers of cells did not induce immunity after being subjected to much lower doses of irradiation. His conclusion was that weak histocompatibility antigens seemed to be much more sensitive to the effects of irradiation than strong ones.[256] A somewhat different result was reached by Monaco and Mandel,[257] who studied the effect of in vitro irradiation on the sensitizing capacity of subcutaneously implanted liver slices as measured by a subsequent test skin allograft of donor origin. These authors found that graded doses of irradiation from 1500 to 2500 r progressively decreased specific sensitization, even when strong histocompatibility antigens were involved. In both experiments the survival and function of the irradiated cells could not be confirmed. It seems that, depending upon the tissue irradiated, the effect of this treatment on transplantation antigens will vary. Certainly, more work in this area of transplantation biology will be necessary.

The significant role of the hematopoietic system in recovery from sublethal doses of total-body irradiation was brought into focus in a series of important papers by Jacobson and his associates.[258-262] These authors showed that shielding portions of the reticuloendothelial system, particularly the spleen, during exposure to total-body irradiation significantly reduced postirradiation mortality. Shielding of the spleen gave the best results although shielding of other areas such as intestine, appendix and hind limb was also effective. These authors[263] favored a theory that attributed recovery to a noncellular factor emanating from the unirradiated areas, the so-called "humoral theory." Subsequently, Lorenz, Congdon and Uphoff[264] demonstrated that, in mice and inbred guinea pigs, infusions of isogeneic bone marrow, after a potentially lethal dose of whole-body irradiation, markedly reduced the mortality observed. The possibility that the donor cells replaced irradiated hematopoietic organs of the host was thus raised, introducing the "cellular theory" of irradiation protection. A number of experiments, interpreted as favoring either one or the other of these theories, were reported until Main and Prehn[265] demonstrated that irradiated DBA mice, injected with (DBA × Balb/C) F_1 bone marrow, permanently accepted and retained grafts of Balb/C skin. They concluded that donor bone marrow not only was responsible for hematopoietic recovery after irradiation, but also determined the survival of subsequent skin allografts. These experiments provided the first strong evidence that injected bone-marrow cells and their progeny continued to survive. Subsequently, serologic evidence was presented by Lindsley and his associates[266,267] that donor erythrocytes were present in the peripheral blood of rats of one strain that had been given bone marrow from another after whole-body irradiation. Ford et al.[268] succeeded in showing that injected rat cells could persist and have hematopoietic function in irradiated mice as xenogeneic grafts. The results suggested that complete replacement of host hematopoietic tissues was achieved by donor cells. Subsequently, persistence of allogeneic and xenogeneic erythrocytes in irradiated mice was independently confirmed by others using serologic methods.[269,270] Thus, the cellular hypothesis had been substantially supported, and the term "chimera," previously used by Anderson et al.[172] to describe animals containing mixtures of genetically different blood cells, was adopted. The concept of the "radiation chimera" emerged. An exhaustive and critical review of this significant aspect of transplantation biology has been presented by Koller, Davies and Doak.[271]

Methods involved in the production of radiation chimeras have been extensively studied and will not be reviewed in detail. Doses of irradiation in excess of 15,000 r result in rapid death from damage to the nervous system. Acute doses of irradiation between 1500 and 15,000 r produce mortality in three or four days as a result of gastrointestinal damage. When total-body irradiation in the range of 400 to 1500 r is delivered death results from complete failure of the hematopoietic system. It is in this lower dose range that bone-marrow infusions are sufficient to rescue treated animals by the formation of irradiation chimeras. The dose of irradiation required to suppress the immune responses sufficiently to permit successful implantation of foreign hematopoietic tissues varies both between strains of the same species and between species.[272] Almost all species of laboratory animals have been utilized, either as irradiated recipients or as donors of hematopoietic tissues. Allogeneic hematopoietic cells have proved moderately effective in reducing the mortality within about thirty days of irradiation in several species, but the mortality has usually been high over more extended periods. The dose of acute irradiation that produces a degree of immune suppression sufficient to permit the survival and proliferation of injected allogeneic hematopoietic tissue in mice is well below that which inevitably results in death from gastrointestinal damage. By contrast, in rabbits and dogs, and probably also in monkeys, it is particularly difficult to establish allografts of hematopoietic tissue, since sufficient suppression of the immune response is difficult to achieve without deleterious gastrointestinal effects. The only successful xenogeneic combination has involved the treatment of irradiated mice with rat hematopoietic cells. This may constitute a special case in which success can be attributed to a relatively high degree of antigenic similarity between rats and mice.[273] Almost all hematopoietic tissues appear to be effective in this regard, and the variability reported is probably due to differing proportions of the various stem cells present in the tissues used.[274] The route of injection is not critical, for any mode of injection of donor cells that is consistent with subsequent rapid migration of a sufficient number of precursors to normal hematopoietic sites appears to be suitable, although the intravenous route is consistently most efficient.[275] The period of maximum suppression of the immune response has been estimated to lie between five and forty-eight hours from completion of a single dose of whole-body irradiation.[276] Although other factors are involved, it thus seems that immediate injection after irradiation provides the best possibility for the rapid function of the transferred hematopoietic tissue graft.

The problem of analysis of irradiation chimeras in terms of donor and host hematopoietic function revolves chiefly about the question of identification of cell genotypes in mixed populations. Chromosome markers have been used extensively. The chromosomes of the rat can be readily distinguished from those of the mouse.[268] A similar opportunity exists in mouse-to-mouse chimeras, in which the distinctive T6 pair of chromosomes[277] is present in either donor or recipient. In rabbits and in man, but not in rats and mice, it is possible to draw a morphologic distinction between granulocytes of the two sexes on the basis of the nuclear configuration of nonmitotic leukocytes. Porter[278,279] utilized this method to identify donor cells in rabbits in which the donor and host were of different sex. The use of this technic is, of course, restricted to species that show a sex difference in granulocyte morphology.[280] Serologic methods detecting well marked antigenic differences between host and donor cells in irradiation chimeras have also been used. A common method has been to test erythrocytes from chimeras for reactivity with hemagglutinins[266,270,281] of known specificity. A number of workers have confirmed the presence of cells of a certain genotype by demonstrating the ability of chimeric tissues to sensitize secondary recipients to appropriate later test grafts.[282] Finally, a number of biochemical methods of identifying cells have been utilized, particularly in rat-to-mouse combinations. These have included differential staining of granulocytes to reveal alkaline phosphatase,[272] specific differences in hemoglobin[283] and differences in electrophoretic patterns of serum proteins.[284]

The progress of repopulation of irradiated hosts by donor cells has been extensively studied. Nowell and his colleagues[285] called attention to the fact that injected hematopoietic cells appeared to proliferate only in sites normally occupied by hematopoietic tissue. This has been referred to as the "homing instinct," and is still incompletely explained. Various types of hematopoietic cells behave differently on injection into irradiated recipients. Injections of isogeneic bone marrow or fetal hematopoietic cells lead to early repopulation of bone-marrow cavities and later to repopulation of lymphopoietic sites. In contrast, isogeneic splenic cells repopulate the spleen more rapidly than the bone marrow.[286] Generally, it appears that the pattern of repopulation is related to the relative proportions of various types of blast cells in the graft. Perhaps a specific homing instinct is present in each type of cell.

Some of the factors involved in determining the period of persistence of donor cells in an irradiated recipient are now known. Although the mouse receiving 950 to 1300 r, followed by injection of rat bone marrow, is usually found to have peripheral blood consisting exclusively of rat cells after a hundred and fifty days, a mouse receiving less than 800 r followed by bone marrow usually does not show persistence of xenogeneic cells but has reverted to peripheral blood of mouse specificity.[287] Reversion of this kind is first obvious in the thymus, then in lymph nodes and then in the spleen and finally in the bone marrow.[288] This is just the reverse of the order of change during the initial process of repopulation. Other studies of rat-to-mouse chimeras[289] revealed that the proportion of mice showing complete or partial reversion increased steadily with time. Various patterns of partial reversion occurred, indicating that in some mice a stable state was obtained with constant proportions of donor and host cells, although it was common for fluctuations in cell proportions to occur. The incidence of reversion is decreased with higher initial doses of total-body irradiation.[289,290] Complete reversion can occur early and rapidly if enough host cells survive the irradiation, or may occur later and more slowly if the number of host cells surviving the irradiation is small. Since the effect of irradiation is to reduce the hematopoietic system to a very small number of viable cells, considerable individual variation can be expected. In allogeneic chimeras the other factors that influence reversion seem to be mainly immunologic.

Delayed mortality of irradiated hosts after hematopoietic-tissue replacement has been observed by a number of workers.[291-294] This delayed mortality had been variously referred to as "secondary disease," "homologous or heterologous disease," "bone-marrow disease" and the "wasting syndrome." The syndrome is not usually observed before thirty days after irradiation and bone-marrow transfer, and is most commonly apparent between twenty-one and seventy days. It involves pathological changes very similar to those seen in runt disease, and they have been summarized in detail.[271]

There is general agreement that the wasting syndrome is fundamentally dependent upon an immunologic reaction, since it occurs only in the presence of antigenic differences between host and donor. Very little evidence exists that the immunologic reaction involved is of the host-versus-graft type.[292,295] More evidence has been accumulated to suggest that it is based upon a graft-versus-host reaction. Barnes et al.[296] found that test skin grafts of donor type were retained by allogeneic mouse chimeras even when the animals were dying of the wasting syndrome. This could not have occurred if the syndrome had primarily been due to a reaction of the host against the graft. Further evidence is the curious phenomenon that mouse-to-mouse chimeras that have received grafts of host and donor type of skin a hundred days after irradiation reject only the host-type skin while donor skin is retained.[297] On the other hand, some workers[222,298] have considered that host-versus-graft and graft-versus-host reactions are both involved in the wasting syndrome.

An interesting piece of evidence supporting the graft-versus-host nature of the wasting syndrome has been sought by experiments attempting to avoid its effects by injection of cells of fetal origin. In these experiments both fetal liver and spleen have been used. Although Congdon and Urso[299] could not prevent the wasting syndrome with fetal bone marrow Uphoff[300] clearly showed that by using fetal liver in mouse chimeras the wasting syndrome was dramatically prevented. This result subsequently was clearly confirmed.[301] Furthermore, Urso et al.[302] reported that bone marrow from such allogeneic chimeras had therapeutic properties similar to that from the original fetal donors. This result implied that tolerance of host antigens induced in the donor fetal tissue was maintained over long periods. It is clear, however, that the degree of success attainable by substitution of fetal for adult tissues depends heavily on the strain combinations used in the experiment. Thus, in xenogeneic chimeras (rat to mouse), no amelioration of the wasting syndrome results from the use of fetal tissue.[303]

The tremendous investigative effort in this area of transplantation biology typified by the experiments described above has provided the foundation for the clinical use of hematopoietic allografts in a number of human diseases. The results of this clinical experience will be described in a later section.

Thymectomy

Although there are many hints in the old literature pointing toward an immunologic role for the thymus, a significant area of transplantation biology was opened by Miller's[304] announcement of a profound impairment in the immunologic development and capacity of mice thymectomized at birth. Similar observations in mice were made independently by Martinez et al.[305] and by Trentin[306] and in rats by Arnason and his colleagues.[307,308]

Thymectomy, performed at a propitious time, has profound effects on the health, longevity and immunologic status of animals. Whereas thymectomy performed at three weeks in many mouse strains has few untoward effects,[309] in neonatally thymectomized mice a syndrome develops at one to three months of age characterized by wasting, lethargy, ruffled hair, hunched back, diarrhea and death within one to three weeks.[310,311] If thymectomy is delayed a few days after birth the severity and incidence of this syndrome decreases. A characteristic anatomic feature of this wasting disease is marked and generalized involution of lymphoid tissue. The similarity of this wasting syndrome to that seen in runt disease, homologous disease in F_1 hybrid mice and secondary disease in radiation chimeras suggests that the incapacity of lymphoid tissues, which is common to them, may be important as an underlying cause.[306] Neonatally thymectomized rats show profound depletion of small lymphocytes, quite obvious in the splenic white pulp and lymph nodes, as well as a depression of circulating lymphocytes.[312] Similarly, in mice, lymphatic tissues are characterized by atrophy, reduced cellularity and few mitoses.[310,313] In both mice and rats the absolute levels of circulating small lymphocytes in the peripheral blood are significantly lower than normal even before the onset of wasting disease.[311,314] Whereas adult thymectomized mice continue lymphocyte production, perhaps at a lower level, it appears virtually to stop in neonatally thymectomized mice.[306]

The effect of thymectomy at various ages on different types of immune responses has now been studied in a number of species. Thymectomy in adult rabbits[315,316] and guinea pigs[317] had no effect on subsequent humoral-antibody formation. On the other hand, rabbits thymectomized within one week of birth,[318] rats thymectomized at birth[308] and neonatally thymectomized mice[311] show a profound impairment in humoral-antibody response to a variety of protein, bacterial and viral antigens. The effect of neonatal thymectomy on delayed hypersensitivity reactions has been studied in rats.[307,308] A marked diminution in the response to bovine serum albumin and tuberculin was found, as well as a loss of ability to develop allergic encephalomyelitis. Depression of delayed reactivity was correlated with diminution in the animals' lymphocyte populations.

Thymectomy in many strains of mice and in rats at birth dramatically impairs the ability to reject subsequent allogeneic and even xenogeneic skin grafts.[304,305,308,319,320] Most grafts grow luxuriant tufts of hair and remain intact until the death of the recipient three or four months later from

87

wasting disease. In the few mice surviving for longer periods the grafts gradually shrink, lose their crops of hair and disappear. The usual signs of rejection, such as edema, reddening, thickening and scab formation, are noticeably lacking. Such mice have no evidence, however, of active immunity to subsequent grafts of donor skin.[311] Thymectomy performed at one week has resulted in some impairment of the allograft response in mice, particularly when the test skin graft involved differed only at the non-H-2 genetic locus. By two weeks of age reactivity was normal except to grafts presenting the weak, sex-linked histocompatibility difference, and by three weeks no impairment of the allograft response could be demonstrated.[320] In the hamster the effects of neonatal thymectomy are similar to those seen in the rat and mouse, except that immunologic impairment is more profound in females than in males.[321] The immunologic impairment produced by neonatal thymectomy is also demonstrated by the fact that cells from lymphoid organs of neonatally thymectomized mice are less able than normal cells to induce a graft-versus-host reaction in appropriate recipients.[302,322] Thus, where 5,000,000 cells from normal mice suffice to produce a reaction, 20,000,000 cells from thymectomized mice are required.

The observation that wasting disease and deficiency of the immune response are associated with thymectomy in early life, but not in adult life, suggests that the most important period of thymic function is restricted to the period before the thymus involutes. Nevertheless, there is evidence that the thymus plays a significant part under special circumstances in adult life. Thymectomy in adult mice is followed by a fall in circulating lymphocytes to as little as 60 to 70 per cent of the normal level. In addition, the weights of spleen and lymph nodes fall by 25 per cent, but small lymphocytes can still be found in the tissues.[323] Mice thymectomized as adults and given a sublethal dose of irradiation two weeks later are unable to reject allogeneic skin grafts when challenged four weeks after irradiation in situations in which weak histocompatibility differences are involved. Furthermore, the humoral-antibody response to sheep erythrocytes was depressed in thymectomized, irradiated mice.[324] Auerbach[325] provided parallel histologic evidence for this immunologic depression when he found that adult thymectomized mice after irradiation do not show a normal rate of recovery of their lymphoid centers when compared with irradiated normal controls. Furthermore, adult thymectomized mice given a lethal dose of irradiation can be protected from acute radiation effects by injection of isogeneic marrow. The number of small lymphocytes in the blood and tissues of such animals is characteristically greatly reduced, and the humoral-antibody and allograft-rejection responses are permanently impaired. Isogeneic chimeras with intact thymuses had normal lymphocyte populations and normal immune responses.[326,327] Added evidence for a role of the adult thymus is the observation of Claman and Talmage[328] that mice rendered tolerant of protein antigens by injection from birth to adulthood lost their tolerance when injections were stopped at a much slower rate if thymectomized as adults. The authors concluded that acquired tolerance comes about by irreversible inhibition of immunologically competent cells, and escape from tolerance occurs by recruitment of new cells, either emanating from the thymus or developing peripherally under its influence.

Thus, the thymus has a profound influence in immunologic development particularly during the neonatal period but also under special circumstances in the adult animal. Such an influence can be by population of lymphoid tissue with small lymphocytes (or their precursors), by cell migration from the thymus or by regulation of lymphocyte production and maturation through a humoral factor. The extremely high mitotic activity in the neonatal thymus provides no more than circumstantial evidence for cell migration from the organ.[306] Nossal's[329] studies with labeling of lymphocytes with radioactive thymidine in adult guinea-pig thymuses revealed that although the degree of labeling and mitotic activity was high, the seeding of cells to other lymphoid organs was quite small. Thus, clear evidence for extensive cell migration is lacking. In an attempt to elucidate the contribution of the thymus to immunodevelopment, extensive studies on restoring the reactivity of thymectomized animals have been carried out. If neonatally thymectomized mice are given injections of normal adult isogeneic lymphnode cells on the fifth day of life the incidence of wasting is decreased, and survivors are immunologically competent. Injections after the first week have no effect.[330] Isogeneic cells from neonatal thymuses, when injected intravenously into newborn mice immediately after thymectomy, fail to restore the immunologic capacity of such animals.[320] Neonatal thymuses, grafted subcutaneously into neonatally thymectomized mice within the first week of life, permanently restore the recipients actively to normal.[311,320] When donor and host are of the same strain the mice reject all foreign skin grafts. When the donor is of a different strain skin neither from the recipient nor from the donor of the thymus is rejected, but third-party skin is rejected normally.[320] Apparently, then, the deficiencies secondary to neonatal thymectomy can be repaired by lymphoid-cell injections from normal mice or by thymus implants.

The efficacy of thymic grafts in restoring immunologic capacity was first attributed to production of lymphocytes by the thymus graft, with subsequent recolonization of host lymphoid tissues, thus producing a lymphoid chimera. Studies utilizing strains of mice with marker chromosomes[277] failed to corroborate this impression. In neonatally thymectomized mice subsequently restored by a subcutaneous thymus graft, the majority of cells in both the host lymphoid tissues and the thymus graft were of host origin, and in many mice cells of only host origin were identified.[330] In mice that were chimeras discriminant assays of the spleen revealed that host cells were responsible for immunologic activity.[331] This finding suggested that the thymus grafts were effective not by actually contributing cells but either by providing a noncellular factor inducing lymphopoiesis or by providing an epithelial, reticular framework into which host cells invaded and found an environment suitable for lymphoid-cell differentiation. The host cells multiplying in the thymus graft would then recolonize the depleted lymphoid tissues of the host. It should be noted in this regard that the majority of the original lymphocytes in a thymus implant are known to degenerate after grafting.[332]

It is clear that cells with immunologic potential exist in the neonatally thymectomized mouse, but that this potential cannot be expressed in the absence of the thymus. Evidence from experiments with irradiated mice suggests that such cells reside in the bone marrow. The condition of lethally irradiated mice can be restored completely by an injection of marrow from normal or thymectomized isogeneic donors. In mice injected with normal isogeneic marrow and lymphoid cells from donors with chromosomal markers the lymphoid-cell marker eventually appeared only in the lymph nodes and was not found either in the thymus or in the bone marrow. The bone-marrow cells appeared in both marrow and thymus. Later, marked lymphoid cells disappeared, and cells of bone-marrow type were found throughout. The suggestion was that cells in the marrow that could differentiate into lymphoid cells resided temporarily in the thymus before passing on to repopulate the lymphoid tissues.[333] In thymectomized, irradiated mice cells in the marrow inoculum could repopulate the marrow, but lymphoid tissues were not recolonized and the animal was immunologically deficient.[327]

Evidence for a thymic influence on lymphoid-tissue development that could be based on a humoral factor was suggested by Auerbach's[334,335] morphogenetic studies. He found that embryonic thymus, isolated and grown in tissue culture, formed lymphocytes in characteristic normal fashion. Embryonic spleen, isolated similarly, did not differentiate further. When the two were combined discrete lymphoid nodules appeared in the spleen. The presence of thymic tissue was required to give this result. Embryonic spleens grown in isolated culture had an appearance strikingly like the spleens of mice thymectomized at birth. Dramatic evidence for a humoral thymic factor was provided by Levey, Trainin and Law,[336] who found that thymus tissue enclosed in Millipore chambers and implanted intraperitoneally into neonatally thymectomized mice prevented the wasting syndrome. Furthermore, the lymphoid organs of such mice did not show the depletion characteristic of thymectomized animals. Mice thymectomized at birth were resistant to the lethal effects of the virus of lymphocytic choriomeningitis, death resulting from a hypersensitivity reaction to the virus demonstrated in normal controls. Implantation of thymus tissue in chambers restored susceptibility to the lethal effects of the virus.[337] Osoba and Miller[338] showed that thymus tissue enclosed in Millipore chambers restored not only the capacity for humoral-antibody formation but also the ability to reject allogeneic skin grafts. Restoration of the capacity for humoral-antibody formation was later confirmed.[339] Finally, it has been demonstrated that the role of the thymus in the recovery of the lymphoid system after sublethal irradiation is mediated by a humoral factor.[340]

It thus appears that although the thymus has a particularly potent directing influence over the entire lymphoid system of young animals, it can be shown to retain certain capacities in the adult. Although centrifugal seeding of cells may have some role in its function clear evidence for a humoral control mechanism has been found.

Chemotherapeutic Modification of the Allograft Response

The modest but significant success of renal allografts in man with the aid of chemotherapeutic agents has given impetus to intensive search for drugs capable of inhibiting the allograft response. A massive and ever growing body of literature already exists on this aspect of transplantation biology alone. So far as the aim of these studies is the uncovering of drugs applicable to human allografting, certain shortcomings in some of the relevant experiments might be mentioned. The ability of drugs to inhibit various types of immune responses in a number of species has been studied. These have included the humoral-antibody response to a standard antigen, the induction of delayed sensitivity reactions and the allograft-rejection reaction. Unfortunately, most drugs are tested for their effect on only one modality of the immune response, usually humoral-antibody formation, even though this frequently does not reflect their effect on allograft survival. Considerable species variation has also been observed, so that the efficacy of a given drug in the clinical setting is difficult to predict. An outstanding example of this is the surprisingly beneficial effect of steroids in human renal transplantation. It seems, therefore, that drug screening, where possible, should include measurement of several modalities of the immune response in more than one species.

In the following paragraphs the various classes of compounds capable of modifying the allograft response are discussed. It should be emphasized that positive experiments must be given greater weight than negative ones, since many studies unfortunately do not utilize maximally tolerated doses of the drugs studied.

Steroids. The effect of corticosteroids (and ACTH) on the immune response has been studied in a number of species. Both hormones have been shown to inhibit anaphylaxis in sensitized rats and mice,[341-343] as well as the development of allergic encephalitis and delayed sensitivity in the guinea pig.[344,345] Steroids also inhibit antibody formation and the Arthus phenomenon in the rabbit.[346] Like irradiation, cortisone appears to have its maximum effects when treatment is begun before the administration of antigen, and little suppressive effect may be detectable if treatment follows antigen injection.[347] For allografts and xenografts the effect of corticosteroids apparently depends on the steroid employed and the species tested. Steroids have been used to suppress rejection of human neoplasms transplanted to xenogeneic hosts,[348,349] the cortisone-treated hamster being widely used for the maintenance of xenogeneic tumor grafts. Cortisone suppresses first-set skin-allograft rejection in the rabbit,[350] guinea pig,[351] mouse[352] and chicken,[353] but has no appreciable effect at ordinary doses in primates.[354] Corticosterone, on the other hand, has little effect on skin allografts in the rabbit.[355] Cortisone prolongs renal-allograft survival in dogs only slightly when used alone[356,357] and does not significantly extend the prolonged survival resulting from other drugs.[358] The clinical observation that high doses of steroids may dramatically abort rejection of human renal allografts stands in sharp contrast to these observations in the dog.[359] The mechanism of this action of corticosteroids on the allograft reaction remains un-settled. Scothorne[360] postulated a failure of anti-gen liberation from the graft and its subsequent transport to immune centers, on the basis of an ef-fect of cortisone on histiocytic activity. On the other hand, effectiveness may be based solely on the ac-tion of steroids as "anti-inflammatory" agents.[361] In-hibition of the inflammatory process would permit the grafted area to remain relatively free of reactive leukocytes, and fibroblastic activity would be held to a minimum, thus protecting the graft by suppress-ing the efferent limb of the allograft reaction. An anti-inflammatory effect alone could help to explain both species differences observed and the variability of action with different steroids. Furthermore, the need for testing the effectiveness of maximally toler-ated doses of newer steroid compounds with marked anti-inflammatory activity is apparent.

Antimetabolites. Interest in the use of antimetab-olites in suppressing the immune response was stim-ulated by the important observation of Schwartz et al.[362] that the antibody response in rabbits to bo-vine serum albumin (BSA) could be completely sup-pressed when 6-mercaptopurine (6-MP) was given during, and for a short time after, a course of im-munization. Neither pretreatment, nor treatment after the immune response, was effective in inhibiting antibody production. In similar experiments with human serum albumin (HSA) high doses of 6-MP resulted in blockage of the primary response but only slight reduction in the secondary response.[363,364] Subsequent experiments showed that specific tol-erance of HSA was produced by vigorous treatment with 6-MP during the first presentation of the antigen. Challenge with antigen (HSA) one and two months later likewise induced no response. Specificity of the tolerant state was demonstrated by the fact that tolerant animals formed antibody to bovine gamma globulin (BGG) when this antigen was given with the second dose of HSA.[365] Other investigators[366-368] have confirmed these findings in rabbits and, in contrast to Schwartz's earlier conclusions, have shown that the secondary response can be suppressed as well.[369,370] Extensive investigations with 6-MP in other species have confirmed its suppressive effect on a number of immune reactions, including delayed reactions in the guinea pig,[371] allergic uveitis in the rabbit,[372] precipitin production in the dog[210] and the reaction to viruses in primates.[373] Sterzl and Holub[374] presented data suggesting that 6-MP was active during the inductive phase of immunity when tested in their cell-transfer system.

Inhibition of standard immune responses by 6-MP naturally led to direct attempts at suppression of the allograft response. Skin allografts are significantly prolonged in the rabbit,[375] rat[376] and mouse.[207] In the latter species genetic relations of donor and host are critical for a positive effect. André et al.[377,378] noted that the usual "hematocytoblasts" found in lymph nodes proximal to skin allografts in rabbits did not appear on 6-MP treatment, nor did rejection occur until these cells were apparent, and the authors postulated an "escape" from 6-MP inhibition to account for subsequent rejection. Calne[379,380] treated dogs with 6-MP and found very significant prolongation of renal allograft survival, but toxicity of the drug rendered management difficult. Zukoski and his co-workers[381-383] and Pierce, Varco and Good[384] had similar results. Several other antimetabolites (8-azaquanine, 6-aza-uracil, azaserine and 5-fluorouracil) did not prolong survival of canine renal allografts.[385] Among drugs directly related to 6-MP, thioquanine and its S-imid-azolyl derivative did not prevent rejection in bone-marrow-depressing doses. Azathioprine* caused less bone-marrow depression while retaining the effectiveness of 6-MP. Others have noted the effectiveness of azathioprine.[386] Combination of azathioprine with other agents did not improve results with the exception of the addition of azaserine, which provided increased survival over that achieved with azathioprine alone.[358,387] The effectiveness of azathioprine in dogs has led to fairly universal use of the drug in human renal allografting. There is evidence that it significantly augments survival of human allografts.[359] The drug appears to have few side effects and can be effective in doses that do not result in bone-marrow depression.

Another antimetabolite extensively tested has been A-methopterin (Methotrexate). This antifolic acid agent inhibits formation of humoral antibody and allograft rejection in both the mouse[388,389] and the guinea pig.[390] In the guinea pig skin-allograft survival was tripled, without prohibitive toxicity. With canine renal allografts, however, A-methopterin did not prolong survival significantly when used alone,[385] nor did it augment prolongation achieved by other drugs.[358] Toxicity seems to be greater in the larger

*Kindly supplied as Imuran (B.W. 57-322) by Dr. George Hitchings, of Burroughs Wellcome and Company (U.S.A.), Incorporated, Tuckahoe, New York.

animals so far tested and probably accounts for the unimpressive results observed.

Alkylating agents. Attempts to modify the immune response by various alkylating agents have been a natural consequence of the observed effect of these agents on lymphoid neoplasms. It was demonstrated fairly early that mechlorethamine (HN_2, nitrogen mustard) could interfere directly with a number of immune responses,[391-393] including hypersensitivity reactions.[394]

In general, alkylating agents (the mustards and ethylene amines) resemble the antimetabolites in that their influence on the immune response is greatest when they are administered with antigen, and for a few days thereafter, rather than beforehand.[388,395] The exceptions to this have been busulfan (Myleran) and L-p-(di-2-chloroethylamino)-phenylalanine (Melphalan), which are capable, like irradiation, of inhibiting the immune response if given before antigen.[396] In general, alkylating agents have been less effective in direct suppression of the allograft response than antimetabolites. Skin allografts in several species were not significantly influenced by mechlorethamine (HN_2) and phenylalanine treatment[397,398] although cyclophosphamide was effective in rabbits[399] and mice.[400] In the latter species the necessity for administration at the time of grafting and shortly thereafter has been demonstrated.[401] Failure to influence the allograft reaction significantly is no doubt due to the toxicity of these compounds at the levels necessary to depress a very strong skin-allograft rejection response. Alkylating agents alone prolong the survival of canine renal allografts very little. Although some prolongation has been reported when they are combined with steroids and splenectomy[402] the overall result of addition of such agents to regimens of known effectiveness (for example, azathioprine) has been to increase the hazard without further benefit.[358]

Antibiotics. The demonstration that certain antibiotics interfere with protein synthesis has led to the use of these agents in attempts to inhibit the immune response, since the latter is a special case of protein synthesis.

The polypeptide antibiotic, actinomycin D, has been extensively studied. This drug affects nucleic acid metabolism in vivo and inhibits DNA-dependent RNA polymerase reactions in vitro,[403] apparently through its capacity to bind with the quanosine groups of DNA. The inhibition of induced protein synthesis results from a blocking in the formation of new messenger RNA.[404] Low concentrations of the drug clearly inhibit secondary responses of previously sensitized lymph-node cells in tissue culture to bacteriophage[405] and protein antigens.[406,407] Jerne, Norden and Henry[405] demonstrated in vivo depression of antibody synthesis in mice. In the rat actinomycin D delays the onset of the immune response but has no effect on the rate or maximum amount of antibody production.[408] Other in vivo studies have demonstrated only a slight suppressive activity toward humoral-antibody formation by either actinomycin D or the related compound actinomycin C.[409] Most of the studies on suppression of the allograft reaction have utilized actinomycin C. This drug alone was ineffective in delaying the rejection of canine renal allografts,[387] and yet it appeared to be effective in aborting incipient rejection when used in conjunction with azathioprine, when it clearly prolonged survival.[358,410] This observation appears to apply to man as well since in many cases treatment with actinomycin C has dramatically interrupted rejection of human renal allografts.[359] Another antibiotic, mitomycin C, is apparently capable of halting RNA synthesis and consequently protein synthesis.[411] As with actinomycin D only DNA-dependent RNA synthesis appears affected. Recently, Bloom et al.[412] demonstrated inhibition of the capacity of sensitized cells to transfer delayed sensitivity after incubation with the drug in spite of maintained viability. Attempts at direct suppression of skin-allograft rejection in mice with mitomycin C have failed.[413] The drug has not been extensively tried in canine renal allografts or in human renal grafting, but its activity against sensitized cells suggests that it may be helpful in management of advancing rejection.

The double indole-indoline alkaloids vincristine (vincristine sulfate) and vinblastine (vincaleukoblastine sulfate), compounds known to be effective growth inhibitors of lymphoid neoplasms,[414,415] were studied for their effect on the immune response by Aisenberg.[416] Clear-cut inhibition of humoral-antibody formation and delayed sensitivity to BSA in rats was demonstrated. Skin allografts were also significantly prolonged. In view of the lack of toxicity of these compounds, as demonstrated in the therapy of human lymphomas, their addition to the immunosuppressive regimen for human renal allografts may be appropriate in the future.

Of the commonly used antibiotics, chloramphenicol has not been as widely studied for its effect on the immune reaction as would be expected from its known interference with protein synthesis in microbial systems. Antibody response to BGG was depressed in rabbits treated with chloramphenicol[417] although the secondary response to diphtheria toxoid in mice was unaffected.[418] In vivo studies of cultured sensitized lymph-node cells clearly demonstrate the capacity of the drug to inhibit the secondary response.[419] The only direct study of its effect on the allograft reaction has been done by Weisberger et al.,[420] who found a definite prolongation of skin allografts in rabbits treated with chloramphenicol.

Graft Adaptation

The phenomenon of adaptation of an allograft to its host has received less attention in the experimental literature than the subject merits, particularly in view of certain isolated and as yet unexplained observations. All the observations described below have as their basis the fact that if an allograft is protected, for a certain time by some artifice, from the immune reaction of the host, the graft appears to become less vulnerable to immunologic attack by the host.

In 1950 Woodruff and Woodruff[35] noted that thyroid allografts established in the anterior chamber of the eye of rats for periods of three to six months could, in a high proportion of experiments, be removed and placed in a subcutaneous site and there become vascularized and survive permanently. This was strong evidence that allografts in some way become less vulnerable after a period of residence in a privileged site within the host.[421,422] A similar situation was described for orthotopic corneal grafts.[37] This loss of vulnerability had not previously been noted for normal tissues although it had long been known to occur in tumor grafts.[4]

Studies on tolerance added further evidence for the existence of some type of adaptive process. Weber, Cannon and Longmire[423] noted in chickens, and Woodruff and Simpson in rats,[424] that skin allografts on animals rendered highly but not completely tolerant could continue to survive without any change in gross appearance whereas a second transplant from the same donor was completely destroyed. In this experimental arrangement the first and second grafts differed in that the latter was in an early state of healing and might have been more vulnerable as a consequence. Billingham et al.[180] suggested that the mechanism for the decreased vulnerability of long tolerated grafts may be due, at least in part, to complete replacement of the vascular endothelium of the transplant by endothelium of host origin. Certainly, a long tolerated skin graft is regularly rejected when transferred to a *normal* member of the recipient strain, indicating retention of sufficient effective antigenicity to provoke rejection even after long periods of residence on the tolerant recipient. This observation was recently reconfirmed in studies on the abolition of tolerance by transfer of sensitized cells.[118]

Stone, Eyring and Kennedy[425] have protected endocrine allografts from host reaction by implantation within Millipore chambers and have made a series of observations supporting Woodruff's contention of an adaptive process. They noted that the grafts in chambers survived well for an initial period, but after prolonged periods of residence (up to thirteen months), the grafted tissue gradually disappeared from the chamber.[425] This was considered to be the result of gradual nutritional deprivation of the graft rather than specific rejection. Puncturing the filter with a fine needle after twenty-five to thirty-five days' residence in the host increased survival of these grafts so that a number of tissues could be successfully transplanted as allografts or even xenografts by this method.[426] Recently, further evidence from this laboratory has shown that after a certain period of residence in the host, the Millipore chamber could be slit several times and reimplanted, with subsequent vascularization of the graft. Survival nevertheless continued.[427] Unfortunately, evidence is not yet available that such long surviving endocrine allografts, although histologically normal in appearance, have retained functional capacity.

Further evidence for some type of adaptive change is suggested by the studies of Murray and his co-workers on dogs with long standing renal allografts maintained by immunosuppressive therapy. For example, a dog with a functioning renal allograft, maintained by treatment with azathioprine and actinomycin C, was grafted with skin from the original kidney donor. The skin graft was fully rejected in three weeks, and yet the kidney continued to function well thereafter.[428] More recently Murray et al.[429] have summarized their experiments on the mechanism of survival of canine renal allograft under drug therapy. Such dogs were capable of rejecting skin and kidney grafts from either indifferent donors or the original kidney donor, indicating persistence of some specific immunological capability. Furthermore, rejection of the second kidney, transplanted from the original donor, took place within forty-eight hours, thus proving the existence of specific host sensitization. Transplantation of the long tolerated kidney to a new, untreated host resulted in prompt rejection, indicating that a non-specific antigenic deletion had not occurred. Other experiments showed that the kidney was no less susceptible than skin to the allograft-rejection process and that no important differences between individual animals in their utilization of drugs could be held responsible for the differing behavior of individuals after receiving transplants. These authors have concluded that the state of tolerance achieved on drug therapy was a "delicately balanced phenomenon specific for the antigen presented at the time drug therapy is started or increased." Although this explains rejection of a third-party allograft while the initial allograft is maintained it cannot explain rejections of allografts of the same genotype. Another unexplained observation is the fact that after prolonged drug therapy, drugs can be withdrawn in isolated cases with maintenance of allograft survival.[384] More experiments of this type are needed in which the genetic relation of the animals involved is controlled and defined.

Critical evidence for true adaptation of allografted tissue is still lacking although studies of tumor-cell populations specific for various inbred strains of mice suggest that this is a possibility. Hauschka et al.[430] reported that repeated passages of a tumor arising in 6 C3HED mice through adult, nontolerant Swiss mice did not produce a tumor lethal to the Swiss host. Koprowski, Theis and Love[431] showed that repeated innoculation of this tumor into *neonatal* Swiss mice, thus inducing specific tolerance, promoted a gradual change in the tumor that resulted in its later ability to grow well in adult Swiss recipients. Evidence was presented that this was an adaptive change in the tumor-cell line, as determined by changes not only in host specificity but also in nucleic acid content of the cells, chromosome modality and susceptibility to viral infection. The authors postulated that a mechanism for transformation or transduction of the original tumor cells may operate similarly to that observed in certain bacteria.[432] They further postulated that transformation of a limited number of cells under the influence of the tolerant host occurred and that selection of these transformed cells may be the second essential step in the observed adaptation. It should be emphasized that if selection of adapted cells is necessary to reveal the phenomenon, studies of allografts composed of rapidly replicating cells, such as lymphocytes or tumor cells, are more likely to be fruitful than experiments with whole-organ allografts composed of nonreplicating cell populations.

Immunologic Deficiency Diseases

A number of human diseases are characterized by deficiency in one or more modalities of the immune response. Studies of these patients have provided an important amount of information on the mechanisms involved in allograft rejection. The entire field of immunologic deficiency diseases is the subject of an important review by Good et al.[433]

Agammaglobulinemia. A number of allotransplantation studies have been carried out in patients with agammaglobulinemia. An initial effort in this area was made by Good and Varco,[434] who transplanted a skin allograft to an agammaglobulinemic child in whom no gamma globulin could be demonstrated by any technic used. The skin graft at no time gave any gross or microscopic evidence of rejection and apparently remained intact and grew with the child for at least six years.[433] Other studies by the same group were carried out in patients with agammaglobulinemia or hypogammaglobulinemia.[435,436] A skin allograft survived for one year in a child with the severe, congenital, sex-linked recessive form of the disease, but after this time, it was slowly rejected. Two adults with acquired agammaglobulinemia received skin allografts, one rejecting the allograft in normal fashion, and the other much more slowly over a period of sixteen weeks. Giedion and Scheidegger[437] studied a child with essentially normal gamma-globulin levels but a deficiency of $beta_2A$ and $beta_2M$ globulins and observed prolonged survival of a skin allograft. Schubert et al.[438] found only slight prolongation of skin allografts in 3 children with congenital agammaglobulinemia. In these children the level of gamma globulin was very low, and the authors concluded that, at least in the human being, allograft immunity is not dependent on normal levels of circulating gamma globulin or the ability to produce humoral antibody. Several studies employing lymphoid-tissue allografts in an effort to re-equip patients adoptively have been performed in agammaglobulinemia. Good and his associates[435] observed take and function of lymph-node transplants over periods of sixty and ninety days in 2 instances, and Martin, Waite and McCullough[439] observed antibody formation by transplanted lymph nodes for a hundred and forty days.

Hodgkin's disease and related lymphomas. The immunologic aspects of Hodgkin's disease have recently been reviewed by Aisenberg.[440] Such patients have a high incidence of tuberculin negativity even in the presence of overt tuberculosis,[441,442] and this unreactivity (anergy) extends to a number of antigens that elicit the delayed-sensitivity response.[443] Whereas cutaneous anergy does occur in the course of various malignant processes such as carcinoma and leukemia, it differs from the anergy seen in Hodgkin's disease in that it occurs late in the course of the disease when the patient is in poor general condition. Studies of patients with Hodgkin's disease, lymphoma other than the Hodgkin type and other malignant and other nonmalignant conditions showed that only in Hodgkin's disease was significant anergy present when the patient was in good overall clinical condition.[444,445] Furthermore, Aisenberg's[446] studies on the induction of contact sensitivity in Hodgkin's disease clearly showed that the anergy present fluctuated with the activity of the disease, a finding suggested in other reports.[445] Of the 33 patients with Hodgkin's disease who have received skin allografts delayed graft rejection has been observed in at least 20.[447-449] Kelly et al.[448] studied the fate of skin allografts on 17 patients with Hodgkin's disease. In the patients tested a small number of grafts behaved essentially as autografts, and a small number were rejected in normal fashion, but the majority survived for three or four weeks before undergoing very slow rejection, frequently taking several months or longer. An interesting finding has been that large skin allografts from parents may survive on their children with Hodgkin's disease essentially as autografts, whereas allografts from unrelated donors enjoy prolonged survival followed by a slow process of chronic rejection.[433,447] An additional observation has been the prolonged survival of allogeneic bone-marrow cells in a patient with Hodgkin's disease.[450] In a small group of patients with lymphomas of various kinds Green and Corso[451] found an inability to reject skin allografts. A possibly related finding is the observation that patients with advanced cancer accepted neoplastic grafts from other patients, which in a few cases grew progressively, whereas such grafts to normal persons were uniformly rejected.[452]

It should be emphasized that the prolonged survival of skin allografts in certain cases of congenital agammaglobulinemia, coupled with the failure of these patients to form antibody, has been offered as strong evidence by Stetson[59] in support of the importance of humoral antibody in the allograft rejection process. Aside from the evidence of Schubert et al.,[438] discussed above, other findings in Hodgkin's disease patients are also relevant. Kelly, Good and Varco[453] found that skin allografts are unusually well tolerated in patients who lack the ability to express delayed allergy but who seem to be capable of producing adequate circulating antibody. The preservation of the capacity to produce antibody in patients with Hodgkin's disease is well documented and has recently been reconfirmed by Aisenberg and Leskowitz.[454]

Sarcoidosis. Studies of patients with sarcoidosis have demonstrated their inability to react to tuberculin.[455] Immunization of such patients with

BCG resulted in fewer conversions to positive tuberculin reactions than BCG immunization of patients without sarcoidosis.[456] Urbach et al.[457] found that in contrast to patients with Hodgkin's disease, tuberculin-negative patients with sarcoidosis, injected intracutaneously with leukocytes from tuberculin-positive donors, are readily converted to tuberculin positivity. The capacity to form circulating antibody, however, is totally unimpaired.[458,459] Skin allografts placed on patients with sarcoidosis enjoy an unusually prolonged survival, although all are eventually rejected.[460]

Ataxia-telangiectasia. Ataxia-telangiectasia is a distinctive syndrome consisting of progressive cerebellar ataxia, oculocutaneous telangiectasia and frequent severe sinopulmonary infections.[461] Recently, the immunologic deficiencies associated with this disease have been emphasized independently by three groups.[462-464] Histologic studies by Peterson et al.[462] revealed abnormalities of lymph-node structure consisting of reticular-cell hyperplasia or decreased cellularity of germinal centers. These authors also emphasized an associated abnormality of the thymus consisting either of its total absence or marked atrophy with only residual epithelial-stromal tissue. Such patients usually show a normal total gamma-globulin content, but immunoelectrophoretic studies have definitely established the common presence of a selective deficiency in $gamma_1 A$ globulins.[462-464] Immunologic studies have demonstrated that patients afflicted with this disorder do not show normal humoral-antibody responses, and a delayed response to a number of standard antigens is lacking. Skin allografts on such patients enjoyed survivals of twenty-four to sixty days.[462] In the 6 cases reported by Peterson et al.[462] 2 patients had reticuloendothelial cancer, and the authors noted that 6 other patients with the syndrome in the literature had an associated malignant tumor. These authors emphasized the fact that the association of an absent or atrophic thymus, immunologic deficiencies and cancer suggests certain similarities to the effects of neonatal thymectomy observed in laboratory animals on immunologic capacity and development (as discussed in an earlier section) and experimental neoplasia.[309]

4

TRANSPLANTATION ANTIGENS

Genetics

The genetics of individual variation is most important to transplantation biology. Allograft rejection is the host's immunologic response directed against genetically determined histocompatibility antigens present in donor tissues and absent in the host. Knowledge of the genetic basis of histocompatibility is derived almost exclusively from experiments performed in highly inbred strains of mice. Inbred strains of other animals are becoming increasingly available and indispensable in transplantation research.[465] At least fifteen histocompatibility loci are known in mice[466,467]; at least four of these loci have been found to exist in established autosomal linkage groups. Two loci, H-1 and H-4, occur in the first linkage group about 24 units apart.[468] H-2 occurs in linkage group IX,[469,470] and H-3 in group V.[469] Studies in "co-isogenic resistant strains" of mice,[471,472] which theoretically differ only in alleles at a single histocompatibility locus, have shown that isoantigens determined by different loci vary in strength. Grafts exchanged between strains differing at the H-2 locus are invariably rejected, with a maximum allograft response in about ten days.[473] Strains differing at the H-1 locus show graft survival for thirty-two to ninety days and at the H-4 locus even longer.[468] The mouse H-2 locus has been the most extensively studied, because it determines not only the strongest transplantation antigens but also the cellular antigens that elicit the production of humoral antibodies detectable as hemagglutinins, hemolysins and cytotoxins.[474,475] At least twenty alleles are involved in the complex H-2 system,[369,476,477] and serologic analysis has demonstrated the existence of more than twenty-five antigenically distinct specificities associated with the antigenic products of these alleles.[474,478] The significance of this dual mode of expression of H-2 antigens — that is, the determination of red-cell and transplantation antigens in the mouse — has not been determined. In both the rat[65,479] and the chicken[480,481] certain loci can determine both histocompatibility and red-cell antigens; yet other loci in both species that determine additional red-cell antigens have no effect on transplantation. Further evidence that transplantation and red-cell antigens do not necessarily have common genetic determinants is the inability to detect products of H-1, H-3 and H-4 loci on red cells of mice.[474]

It has been found that isografts of skin[482] and other tissues[483] from males to females of certain strains are not permanently accepted. The rejection that occurs is due to histocompatibility factors associated with the Y chromosome. Two tenable explanations for this phenomenon exist: either an orthodox histocompatibility locus is responsible[212] or the heterochromatic portion of the Y chromosome itself possesses antigenic activity.[239]

The multiplicity of histocompatibility loci demonstrated in mice has been found to exist also in rats,[465] guinea pigs,[484] rabbits[11] and probably man.[485]

Relation of "T," "E" and "H" Antigens

Methods of assay. A point long at issue has been the relation between histocompatibility antigens and hemagglutinogens as mentioned above. Two possibilities have been considered. The first is that a single class of isoantigens is determined at H-2 and that these antigens are shared by erythrocytes and tissue cells, manifesting themselves in serologic work as blood-group antigens and in transplantation studies as histocompatibility antigens. This is the so-called "one-gene, one-antigen" hypothesis. An alternate possibility is that two classes of isoantigens are determined at the H-2 locus, one with the properties of hemagglutinogens and the other constituting the histocompatibility or transplantation antigens. Until recently the latter view was generally held to be sound, since most evidence indicated that "H" antigens (hemagglutinogens) and "T" antigens (transplantation antigens) had both different tissue distribution and physical properties, besides possessing qualitatively different immunogenicity.[486] "H" antigens were thought to be present on erythrocyte and other cell membranes, more stable to lyophilization and capable of inducing hemagglutinin production and the "enhancement" of skin grafts rather than transplantation immunity. "T" antigens, in contrast, were considered to be absent from erythrocytes but present on tissue cells, labile to lyophilization and capable of inducing transplantation immunity without humoral hemagglutinating-antibody formation.[1,487,488]

As more studies on cell-free preparations with H-2 specificity are reported, it is becoming increasingly apparent that a distinction between "T" and "H" antigens is artificial. Various methods of assay of these antigenic preparations are available. The biologic assay of accelerated skin-graft rejection measures the ability of preparations to sensitize to a subsequent skin graft ("T" antigens). Despite previous contrary evidence,[488] it is now established that cell-free antigenic preparations that provoke skin-graft sensitivity also frequently elicit the formation of humoral antibodies, demonstrable as hemagglutinins and hemolysins.[489] Such preparations can inhibit agglutination and lysis of appropriate red cells by isoimmune serum as well as inhibit the cytotoxic effect of immune serum on allogeneic lymphoid cells in vitro.[490] Thus, serologic reactions, particularly hemagglutination inhibition,[491] have undoubtedly furnished sensitive methods of assay for use during extraction and purification of cell-free histocompatibility gene products. Such antigenic preparations are referred to in the literature as "H" (hemagglutinogen) antigens although their ability to sensitize as transplantation antigens is well established. A third immunologic phenomenon mediated by this humoral antibody produced by H-2-determined isoantigens is enhancement (as discussed above). Assays of cell-free antigenic preparations with H-2 specificity can be based on the ability of the preparation to enhance subsequent tumor grafts ("E" antigens). In addition to the direct biologic test, hemagglutination inhibition and hemagglutinogenic activity can be used for assay purposes.[492]

Each method of assay has certain deficiencies.

The biologic assays of transplantation sensitivity and enhancing ability take time. Although a linear dose-response curve can be obtained with the accelerated skin-graft assay, when less than maximally sensitizing doses are used, the dose-response effect is not sensitive, and quantitative critical assay is difficult.[493] Hemag-glutination inhibition measures only a haptenic function of the histocompatibility antigen, so that the antigen can be degraded in preparation and still give a positive assay.

Development and Tissue Distribution of Transplantation Antigens

Since all tissues are derived from a multipotential cell that contains all genetic information the important question arises whether such information is equally expressed in all tissues. This concept also has an important bearing on the question of the fetus as an allograft; this subject is covered in a recently published review by R. E. Billingham.[494] Information bearing upon the development and distribution of transplantation antigens derives either from biologic experiments, in which intact tissues are used, or from tests of the comparative potency of antigens extracted from various tissues.

When the strains of inbred mice involved differ at the H-2 locus no difference in survival time of various tissues is usually found. Thus, skin and ovary grafts exchanged across an H-2 locus are rejected rapidly and with equal intensity.[495,496] Likewise, both types of grafts exchanged between strains differing at multiple, non-H-2 or weak antigenic loci show equal antigenicity. However, an ovarian graft between certain strains differing at the weak H-1 locus is frequently accepted longer than a corresponding skin graft.[468] Furthermore, in certain weak combinations ovarian grafts not only escape rejection entirely but also may actually condition the host to accept a skin graft that would ordinarily be rejected.[496] Prior immunization abolishes this conditioning effect. Other tissues — for example, testis — have not so far been found to demonstrate this preconditioning effect. Similarly, Russell and Gittes[497] provided functional and histologic evidence that in certain rat strains, parathyroid grafts survived much longer than skin grafts of the same genotype. The preconditioning effect noted with ovarian grafts, however, was not observed. A similar functional antigenic deficiency appears to exist in the specialized trophoblastic cells of the placenta that may be an important part of the natural provision for long-term intimate contact of mammalian mother and fetus, even though they commonly differ genetically.[498] There is also some evidence that H-2-determined antigens cannot be detected on spermatozoa, at least by immunofluorescent methods.[499] Clearly, then, depending on the genetic relations involved and the tissues studied, the expression of histocompatibility genes may vary in some way as yet unexplained.

The ontogeny of antigenic differences between strains of mice has been studied by a variety of methods. Utilizing accelerated skin-graft rejection as a test for antigenicity, Billingham et al.[500] and Chutná and Hašková[501] detected transplantation antigens in the eleven-and-a-half-day and eight-day mouse embryo respectively. Subsequently, antigens were demonstrated in the one-day embryo. Several investigators, employing serologic technics, failed to demonstrate "H" antigens in mouse tissues until

shortly after birth.[502-504] The discrepancy suggests
the possibility that during development, antigens capable of eliciting humoral antibody appear later
than antigens responsible for transplantation immunity. This argues against the evidence presented
above that "T" and "H" antigens are a single biochemical entity.[489] Recently, Möller[505] demonstrated
antibody-absorbing antigens in embryos older than
fifteen days, and Doria[506] found transplantation
antigens in the hematopoietic tissue of mouse embryos of the same age. The time coincidence of these
two operationally different expressions of antigenicity
is in full agreement with the concept that only one
type of strain-specific antigen exists. Repeated attempts to detect antigens in very young embryos have
been unsuccessful; this could be due either to lack of
sensitivity of the assay method or to late activation of
the genes controlling their synthesis (perhaps on the
model for gene derepression suggested by Monod and
Jacob[507]). The studies of Simmons and Russell[498]
clearly demonstrate development of transplantation
antigens shortly after the first week of gestation.

The maturation of H-2 isoantigens in the liver
and spleen of developing mice was studied by Basch
and Stetson,[508] utilizing their quantitative cytotoxic
assay. Significant amounts of antigen were found on
the first day of life. Between the third and fifth days
a marked increase in antigen activity occurred, and
by the ninth day, values greater than 50 per cent of
the adult levels were found. Until the fifth day of
life the antigen activity of the liver exceeded that of
spleen. Shortly thereafter the adult pattern, in which
the activity of spleen is considerably higher than
that of liver, was reached.

The distribution of histocompatibility antigens in

the various tissues of adult animals has been the subject of several studies. Barnes[509] showed that minute grafts of every intact tissue studied could sensitize the recipient to a subsequent skin graft. The H-2 isoantigen content of mouse tissues has been studied quantitatively by hemagglutination inhibition[502] and cytotoxin inhibition[490,510] with comparable results. Spleen, thymus, liver, lymph nodes and bone marrow have a high isoantigen content, with lesser amounts in kidney and muscle, and still less in erythrocytes, brain and placenta. The ability of various tissues to sensitize to a subsequent skin graft seems to correlate with their content of isoantigens detectable serologically. The singular exception to this is the erythrocyte. It appears, at present, that preparations of pure red cells are incapable of sensitizing to skin allografts. Many believe that contrary findings[511] are possibly due to leukocyte contamination.[13] Since H-2 isoantigens are present on erythrocytes and it is the current consensus that "T" and "H" antigens have the same specificity, the observation that erythrocytes cannot sensitize is, as yet, unexplained.

Subcellular Localization of Histocompatibility Antigens

Very few attempts to localize histocompatibility antigens in intact cells have been reported. Möller[512] demonstrated by immunofluorescence the presence of H-2 isoantigens on the outer cellular membranes of lymphoid cells although no information on intracellular localization could be obtained.

The majority of studies have employed standard methods of cell fractionation, with subsequent assay of the various fractions by the accelerated skin-graft rejection reaction or by serologic methods. Early experiments suggested that antigenic activity was closely associated with intact nuclei or nuclear fragments,[500,513] and that possibly deoxyribonucleic acid or deoxyribonucleoproteins were responsible for transplantation immunity. Subsequent studies, however, revealed that preparations of undegraded DNA were only feebly antigenic, presumably on the basis of contamination with antigenic impurities.[514,515] Certainly, evidence against an exclusive nuclear localization of transplantation antigens is the recent demonstration that blood platelets, which are devoid of nuclear material, contain transplantation antigens.[516-518]

Recently, several laboratories have utilized ultracentrifugation to determine the distribution of antigenic activity in mouse-liver and lymphoid-tissue homogenates. Because of differences in starting material, suspending medium, methods of homogenization, extraction and fractionation, as well as assay technics, uniformity of conclusions has been lacking. Utilizing a hemagglutination-inhibition assay, Herzenberg and Herzenberg[519] found antigenic activity in the cell-membrane fractions of liver cells. Basch and Stetson[508] reported that most antigenic activity was associated with the mitochondrial (light and dense) fractions, and the presence of acid phosphatase activity in the active fractions suggested that much of the intracellular antigen may be associated with lysosomes. Only a small amount of activity was found in the nuclear and microsomal fractions. Other studies, utilizing a variety of assay methods, have demonstrated the presence of antigenic activity in several subcellular fractions.[520-522]

Manson et al.[523,524] take a contrary view. They believe that antigenic activity is confined to the microsomal fraction, specifically the microsomal lipoproteins. This result was achieved by the homogenization of cells by nitrogen-bomb decompression, a procedure known to disrupt internal cellular membranes. Manson has argued that reports demonstrating antigen in a variety of subcellular fractions are based on serologic assays in which haptenic fragments could be detected as antigen. Recently, in our laboratory, splenic-tissue homogenates were prepared in a standard manner without nitrogen-bomb decompression, and the ultracentrifuge fractions were assayed for the presence of antigen by accelerated skin-graft rejection.[525] Antigen was found dispersed over several subcellular fractions, the majority sedimenting with a density between mitochondria and microsomes, in close agreement with the results described by Basch and Stetson.[508]

The majority of experiments, to date, suggest that histocompatibility antigens are associated with both the external-cell membranes and internal membranous components of various cell organelles. Obviously, interpretation of subcellular-fraction studies would be facilitated by knowledge of the distribution of cell-surface membrane material in the various fractions, but adequate information on this point is still lacking.

Methods of Preparation and Properties of Histocompatibility Antigens

Cell-free transplantation antigens, assayed by accelerated skin-graft rejection, have been studied extensively by Medawar and his colleagues.[526] These workers originally exposed disrupted lymphoid cells to graded doses of ultrasound in distilled water. Centrifugation of this crude aqueous extract at 27,700 xg for forty-five minutes revealed antigenic activity equally divided between sediment and supernatant. Subsequent centrifugation of this supernatant at 173,000 xg still left traces of antigen in the supernatant. If, however, the supernatant was adjusted to a concentration of 0.15 N sodium chloride and centrifugation at 27,700 xg was repeated, most of the activity appeared in the sediment. Antigenic fragments apparently aggregate in the presence of electrolytes. Medawar has defined two antigenic preparations, the "crude aqueous preparation," an aqueous homogenate made up to a concentration of 0.15 N sodium chloride spun at 5000 xg for ten minutes to remove the DNA protein, and the "antigenic sediment," derived from centrifuging the crude aqueous preparation at 30,000 xg for sixty minutes. The chemical composition of this grossly impure antigenic sediment has been found to be approximately 60 per cent protein and 35 per cent lipid, with small amounts of ribonucleic acid, deoxyribonucleic acid and various sugars and amino sugars, including glucosamine and galactosamine. Activity could be associated with any of the major moieties, protein, lipid or carbohydrate. Enzymatic analysis has demonstrated that activity is resistant to the action of ribonuclease, deoxyribonuclease, alpha and beta amylases, hyaluronidase, lysosome, neurominidase and, to a variable extent, proteolytic enzymes.[81,217,527]

The chemical analysis and purification of transplantation antigens has been hindered by inability to prepare a soluble product that retains antigenic activity. Exposure of Medawar's antigen[526] to triton 100 or sodium deoxycholate destroys antigenicity. Although this implicates the lipid component as the moiety determining antigenic activity, such a conclusion is rendered questionable by the fact that antigen and detergent must be injected together in the biologic assay. Extraction of the antigenic sediment with lipid solvents resulted in a lipid-soluble fraction that did not sensitize and a residue that retained some sensitizing activity but did not absorb humoral antibodies. Reconstitution of the two fractions gave the same results as the residue alone. Studies of heat stability surprisingly demonstrated that some portion of antigen survived exposure to 100°C. for ten minutes, detected as sensitizing power, although ability to combine with humoral antibodies was lost. The last two observations are best explained by the assumption that the antigen preparation so isolated is composed of a chemically heterogeneous assemblage of molecules, some of which are labile or resistant to lipid solvents as well as to heat.

It is now apparent that transplantation antigens prepared in sucrose solutions are quite potent as measured by the skin-graft rejection assay. Manson et al.[524] have isolated an active antigenic material from a DBA/2 lymphoma cell line[523] and normal DBA/2 splenic cells.[524] The microsomal fraction was isolated from cells homogenized in 0.25 M sucrose and then decompressed in a nitrogen bomb. This fraction was then homogenized in 1.5 M sucrose and subjected to ultracentrifugation. Almost all the activity was found in a pellicle at the surface of the supernatant in the centrifuge tube. Suspensions of this material retain activity for one week at 5°C.

Preliminary findings indicate that this material is a complex lipoprotein, presumably associated with the cell membrane and endoplasmic reticulum. The material has properties similar to those of the high-density lipoprotein components of normal serum. Its chemical composition is similar to that of Medawar's antigenic sediment. The antigen extracted from as little as 5 mg. of splenic tissue causes significant sensitization. Monaco et al.,[525] utilizing a much simpler method of preparation, confirmed this potency and found that antigen extracted from C57 mouse-spleen cells in sucrose solution is remarkably stable to freezing and lyophilization for periods of a month or more. Mannick[20] has made the interesting observation that the tissue-culture fluid recovered from rabbit-spleen cell cultures contains transplantation antigens that are similarly stable to freezing and lyophilization.

Studies of the isohemagglutinogens determined by the H-2 locus have given results essentially similar to those described above. The Herzenbergs[519] isolate all the hemagglutinin-absorbing activity of liver cells homogenized in sucrose solution in the fractions containing the cellular and nuclear membranes. The material can be stored in the cold, and is thermolabile at 100°C. Studies of its chemical composition showed it to be almost entirely lipid and protein, with less than 1 per cent carbohydrate. Although hemagglutinogenic in mice, it does not elicit transplantation immunity. The significance of this matter is discussed below.

Davies[528] has studied H-2 antigens in mice utilizing a hemagglutination-inhibition assay. In his experiments large volumes of ascitic fluid obtained from mice with strain-specific tumors served as the source of antigenic material. He thus sought to avoid the contaminating substances present in cell homogenates. By fractional precipitation with distilled water and then dialysis against buffers, followed by fractionation against density gradients, a highly active (thousandfold increase over starting material), readily dispersible but insoluble material was obtained. This material is hemagglutinogenic[529,530] and is apparently capable of conferring sensitivity to skin grafts. Weak antigens, determined at a non-H-2 locus, can be isolated by this method.[531] The antigen was found to have the same lability to wide ranges of pH as other preparations of transplantation antigens described above.[525,526] In contrast to the transplantation antigens assayed by skin-graft rejection, however, this material was remarkably labile to freezing and lyophilization, brief exposure to 60°C. and ultrasonic irradiation. Attempts to render it soluble with various mediums destroyed activity. Exposure to 1 per cent Tween 80 and extraction with organic solvents similarly destroyed activity. Chemical studies demonstrated the material to be a lipoprotein, and in the course of purification, lipid content increased with increased serologic activity.[532]

Kandutsch and Stimpfling[533,534] have studied the antigens with H-2 specificity responsible for immunologic enhancement. Previous experiments had shown enhancing antigen to be widely distributed throughout fractions of tissue homogenates, presumably in membranous particles.[520] The most potent material was found in a residual fraction insoluble in both water and salt solutions. Subsequently, a water-insoluble particulate fraction was isolated from sarcoma I cells in distilled water. This was then exposed to RNAase and DNAase. After the nucleic acids had been digested, the antigenic activity was isolated from the particulate fraction by prolonged exposure (ten to fourteen days) to 5 per cent triton. After extraction, the material could be recovered free of triton by precipitation with cold acetone. Extraction of the acetone-precipitated material with aqueous salt solutions left an active water-insoluble precipitate, termed the "triton-soluble lipoprotein." This material was hemagglutinogenic and could inhibit hemagglutination. Moving boundary and zone electrophoresis suggested that the material was a homogeneous lipoprotein. An interesting finding was that exposure of the antigen to snake venom rendered it water soluble. Electrophoresis of this altered material then revealed both a major and a minor component. Hemagglutinating-antibody activity was retained. This suggests that one part of the triton-soluble lipoprotein molecule, as isolated, was not necessary to achieve the immunologic effect described. It should be noted that most preparations of enhancing antigens, even when incorporated in Freund's adjuvant, do not provoke sensitivity to skin grafts although there is some evidence that weak sensitization can be achieved in certain genetic combinations.[535]

The accumulated studies of various histocompatibility-antigen preparations with H-2 specificity suggest that there is no longer any justification for making a distinction between transplantation ("T") antigens and hemagglutinogens ("H"). Furthermore, it seems certain that the specificity of the H-2 locus, as determined by enhancing, sensitizing or hemagglutinating activity, resides in a lipoprotein (or glycolipoprotein) complex that is an integral part of cellular membranes. Certain basic questions remain unanswered. It is not known whether the multiple specificities of a single H-2 allele are expressed on single macromolecules or individually on different molecules. Further progress in biochemical elucidation of this problem will be seriously handicapped until active soluble preparations are at hand.

Clearly, differences in physical properties exist. Antigenic preparations with sensitizing and enhancing activity can be frozen and freeze-dried with impunity, whereas hemagglutinogenic antigens cannot. Enhancing antigens can be lipid extracted, but the other preparations lose activity with this treatment. Hemagglutinogens are labile to ultrasound, whereas transplantation antigens are not. Another observation difficult to explain is the failure to extract antigenic material with sensitizing power from certain types of cells, such as liver, although material with serologic activity can be recovered.[519] With the same extraction procedure antigenic material with sensitizing and serologic activity can be extracted from lymphatic tissues.[524] This could be accounted for if the H-2 locus imprints its specificity on different species of macromolecules. Then the physical size of molecular aggregates, or the presence of certain subsidiary molecular groups,[530] may be an important factor in determining whether the preparation will evoke sensitivity to allografts as well as display serologic activity. The observation that sediments of preparations with sensitizing power are commonly more active than the mother liquor from which they are derived suggests that mere physical size of the molecular aggregate increases sensitizing power.[526] The problem of failure to extract sensitizing antigens from the liver has recently been analyzed by Mandel et al.[536] Clear-cut evidence has been obtained for the presence in the liver of an enzyme, stable at 60°C. and labile at 80°C., that is capable of destroying sensitizing antigens extracted from splenic tissue. It therefore seems that failure to extract sensitizing antigens from the liver, even though serologic activity is preserved, is due to enzymatic degradation during the extraction procedure of the portion of the lipoprotein complex that confers sensitizing power.

5

EXPERIMENTAL AND CLINICAL ORGAN TRANSPLANTATION

Experimental Organ Transplantation

Much experimental work has been done in the technical realm of organ transplantation. Although some of these efforts antedated Carrel and Guthrie, their ingenious exploratory work,[537] early in this century, ushered in the present era. Their work included the grafting of the entire head of a puppy to the cervical vessels of a larger recipient dog, the reimplantation of canine extremities and the transplantation of kidneys.

In recent years further advances have been made as special attention has been paid to the technical problems surrounding transplantation of a wide variety of organs and of whole extremities. The transplantation of each organ raises a peculiar set of technical challenges and provides special opportunities for physiologic observations. Inevitably, transplanted organs are deprived of extrinsic nervous connections and, at least temporarily, of lymphatic drainage.

In general, the period of effective, functional survival of allogeneic organs transplanted with primary vascular union is roughly of the same order of magnitude as the survival of implanted organ fragments or of skin grafts in the same genetic circumstances. A typical inflammatory cellular infiltrate, often centering about venules, is regularly associated with the rejection process, and major vascular thrombosis is not a primary cause of organ necrosis in previously unsensitized recipients, although stasis in smaller vessels regularly occurs in the advanced stages of rejection.

Endocrine tissues lend themselves particularly well to *implantation* technics in which free fragments of tissue are placed in richly vascularized sites — for example, within the substance of a muscle. Effective blood vascular supply is usually achieved by the third or fourth day.[27] The fact that normal function of a variety of endocrine tissues has been achieved experimentally where autografts are concerned makes it doubtful if surgically constructed vascular anastomoses to whole endocrine organs will add any important technical advantage to this approach in the use of allografts.

Detailed accounts of the individual technical questions pertaining to the transplantation of each organ, where transfer of a large mass of organized tissue is necessary, must lie outside the range of this report. Nevertheless, satisfactory solutions to them are obviously essential to the practical application in surgery of the more general biologic knowledge that we are considering here. For example, the triple blood supply of the *liver* and *lung* offer particular questions regarding the hemodynamic relations between organ and recipient. Complete removal and autologous reimplantation of the canine lung (without reanastomosis of the bronchial arterial supply) is associated with definite and prolonged loss of function in most cases,[538,539] even though some lymphatic regeneration can be detected in two or three weeks. Responsibility for reduced function has not been assigned conclusively to one or another of the possible mechanisms. In other species, however, this is less true, so that transplantation as presently performed does not involve sufficient interference with the normal vascular and nervous connections to preclude satisfactory function. Recently, Barnes et al.[540] detailed the histologic sequence of canine-lung allograft rejection. These authors found prominent perivascular round-cell infiltration beginning on the fourth day, with a peak by the eighth day. Coincident with this was intra-alveolar edema and cell infiltration, terminating in massive necrosis and hemorrhage of the entire allograft, without evidence of thrombosis at eight to eleven days. Functional studies utilizing peripheral determinations of arterial oxygen tension indicate that functional impairment correlated with the anatomic alterations. Dogs treated with azathioprine showed a marked attenuation of this process, and prolonged survival of lung allografts was achieved.[541]

Transplantation of the *liver* was first studied in the dog by heterotopic transfer of the whole organ[542] and subsequently by insertion of the transplant in its normal position as an orthotopic graft.[543,544] Although graft-versus-host activity might be expected where a considerable mass of reticuloendothelial tissue is transferred, this has not been definitely identified during the onward course of rejection. It has so far been very difficult to extend survival of such recipients beyond about three weeks even with a variety of immunosuppressive drugs and full supportive treatment.[545]

Orthotopic transplantation of the *spleen* has also been studied without revealing distinguishable systemic effects that might be attributable to graft-versus-host activity.[546,547] Splenic transplantation has been unsuccessful in rescuing dogs from the effects of whole-body irradiation in the lethal range.[548]

The extensive literature pertaining directly to experimental *kidney* transplantation has been summarized in a recent volume.[549] Heterotopic transplantation has proved to be most convenient with this organ, transplantation either to the neck (in the original style of Carrel) or to the iliac fossa being the most commonly used technic. The first full descriptions of the behavior of canine kidneys on allotransplantation were furnished by Dempster[224] and by Simonsen.[225] Although a transplanted kidney usually functions quite promptly, often beginning with a varying period of diuresis, it is remarkable that the function of this organ is not more radically altered in view of its lack of nervous connections and especially with the change in interstitial pressure relations that should occur with interruption of lymphatic drainage.[550]

The particularly demanding technical problems concerned in transplantation of the *heart* have likewise been substantially overcome, so that it is possible to place a functioning heart either in its normal location in the vascular tree or elsewhere. The immunologic reaction to a transplanted heart develops rapidly, with perivascular infiltrating cells becoming apparent in three to five hours.[551] Ramos et al.[552] observed marked vascular permeability in canine cardiac allografts one hour after transplantation. This permeability could be duplicated in isolated hearts perfused with cell-free plasma from dogs that had previously rejected cardiac allografts. The authors concluded that a humoral factor could be operative quite early in cardiac allograft rejection. Nevertheless, survival of a dog for as long as forty-two days has been recorded to follow orthotopic cardiac transplantation and treatment with A-methopterin.[553]

The *small intestine*[554] and the *stomach*[555] have also proved to be amenable to transplantation by modern technics, which have recently been summarized by Lillehei.[556]

Histocompatibility Testing

It is reasonable to expect that man, like other species, possesses both "strong" and "weak" histocompatibility antigens.[471,472] In mice the number of strong histocompatibility antigens has proved to be less than the number of weak ones, as is true of the erythrocyte isoagglutinogens in the human being. Much work is currently being done to explore various methods of detecting histocompatibility differences between individuals. There is hope that it will be possible actually to characterize the individual-specific antigens of the human population. From all current understanding, some finite number of antigens must be distributed in the human population so that certain individuals, by chance, must share antigens of identical specificity.

The likelihood that two individuals will have identical representations of histocompatibility antigens clearly diminishes rapidly with the number of responsible genes segregating independently, and is dependent upon the proportion of the population in which each component factor is present. A full mathematical analysis of the chance of encountering complete compatibility with varying numbers of antigens has been made by Newth,[557] taking into account the greater similarity that exists between siblings or between parents and offspring. Lacking knowledge of the number of *strong* antigens in the human population, estimates of this sort are probably overly pessimistic, since animal experiments have shown that the reaction expected when the differences involved do not include strong antigens is much milder.

More gross estimates of total histocompatibility differences between individuals may be possible without full characterization of antigens. For example, one can make a crude estimate of antigenic *similarity* by transferring a test skin allograft from the eventual intended recipient to an indifferent individual and following this with a battery of grafts from intended donors. The graft in the latter group that meets destruction first can then be said to have come from the donor who *shared* the greatest number of operative antigens with the donor of the first graft, the eventual recipient. Experiments of this design, which derived originally from the work of Rapaport et al.,[558] have since been applied by others[559,560] as histocompatibility tests. They have the decisive drawback of being incapable of revealing *differences* in antigenic makeup. They do, however, obviate specific sensitization of the intended recipient as occurs with the direct transfer of a preliminary test graft from donor to recipient.

The requirements for a satisfactory test of histocompatibility have recently been summarized as follows by Brent[561] at a conference devoted to this subject:

(i) It should exclude from any given panel of potential donors, whether small or large, those whose organs would elicit a particularly violent response, i.e. it should act as an exclusion test; (ii) it should pinpoint the individual whose tissues would be tolerated for the longest time, i.e. it should act as a selection test; (iii) it should not lead to sensitization of the future recipient; (iv) it should be quick to execute and have a high degree of discrimination; (v) it must not be subject to disqualification because the patient is uremic or otherwise debilitated and, (vi) it should be applicable to cadaver donors.

A recent new approach to the problem of a screening test was inaugurated by Brent and Medawar.[562] Their test, the *normal lymphocyte transfer test* (N.L.T.), was done in guinea pigs. They first removed a population of potentially responsive cells from the intended recipient by separating living lymphocytes from the peripheral blood. A standard number of these cells was then injected intracutaneously into a panel of potential donors. Erythematous wheals developed at the lymphocyte injection sites, reaching maximal size after about forty-eight hours, and were believed to be on the basis primarily of graft-versus-host reactivity. This supposition was strengthened by the correlation between the size of skin reactions and the survival time of skin grafts subsequently returned to the cell

137

The Biology of Tissue Transplantation

donors. Fairly similar findings for man have been arrived at by Gray and Russell,[563,564] who believe that their results support the graft-versus-host nature of the forty-eight-hour reaction in man and that the magnitude of the reaction is a helpful measure of histocompatibility differences, although the test is clearly not a highly sensitive one (Figs. 15, 16c, d). They have used it in 4 cases to aid in selecting a donor for kidney transplantation, with very satisfactory initial results.

Another method, similar in concept to this approach, has recently been described. In this *in vitro leukocyte stimulation test* blood leukocytes from 2 donors are placed in mixed culture for a period of several days. Mitotic activity, the development of large basophilic cells, the release of gamma globulin into the medium[565] and the incorporation of tritiated thymidine by dividing cells[566] have all been described as possible quantitative measures of histocompatibility differences (Fig. 16e, f). At present this test, although depending on a phenomenon of great interest and potential importance, is still untried. The fact that cells taken from persons who have previously exchanged skin grafts do not appear to stimulate one another appreciably more than those from normal donors may suggest that the reactivity seen is less closely allied with the allograft response than is to be hoped.[567] The mutual reactivity between cells of the two genotypes in mixed cultures that can be expected to occur is also a drawback to the use of the test in its present form as a measure of unidirectional differences.

Although such screening tests of compatibility may be very valuable, for the present it seems likely that they will eventually give way to serologic methods that will actually identify histocompatibility antigens, probably by the use of conveniently available leukocytes as a source of antigens. Work is now progressing rapidly in this field, but the imposing task that lies ahead will surely take time. Among the obstacles in this very demanding area are the difficulties of preparing monovalent antiserums, the development of an optimally sensitive and reproducible system for measuring antibody and, finally, the determination of the possible biologic role of each of the antigens identified in this way.

Nevertheless, it is already apparent, particularly from the work of Van Rood and van Leeuwen[568,569] and Payne et al.,[570] that a number of leukocyte groups with appropriate alleles have been identified by means of leukoagglutination testing of antiserums derived mainly from post-partum women.

This important area of research has now become one of the more active in the field of transplantation immunology.

Clinical Transplantation

The objective common to all clinical applications of transplantation is, of course, to make up for lost physiologic function that may result from tissues missing or destroyed. As indicated above, some tissues are capable of exercising their normal functions even though moved to a different region of the body and even under circumstances when their blood supply springs only from tiny vessels that find their way to the grafted tissue in the normal course of healing.

Endocrine tissues. Endocrine tissues can be quite

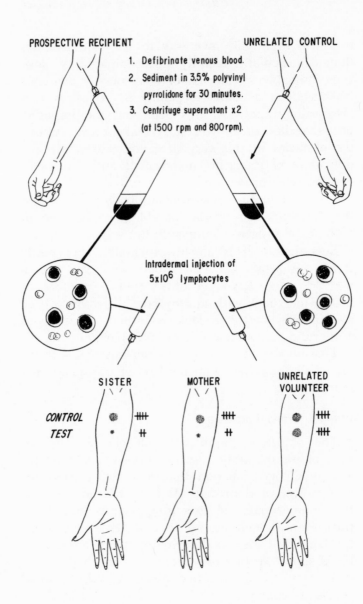

PROSPECTIVE RECIPIENT   UNRELATED CONTROL

1. Defibrinate venous blood.
2. Sediment in 3.5% polyvinyl
   pyrrolidone for 30 minutes.
3. Centrifuge supernatant x2
   (at 1500 rpm and 800 rpm).

Intradermal injection of
5x10⁶ lymphocytes

SISTER   MOTHER   UNRELATED
                            VOLUNTEER

CONTROL
TEST

FIGURE 15. *The Normal Lymphocyte Transfer Test (N.L.T.)
in Man as Performed by Gray and Russell.*[563,564]

This test estimates histocompatibility differences between a
prospective recipient of an allograft and a panel of possible
donors.

In this figure venous blood is drawn from the prospective
recipient and an unrelated control person. Both samples are
processed in parallel in the following manner. The blood is
defibrinated and mixed with 3.5% polyvinyl pyrrolidone
(PVP) in a ratio of 1 part PVP to 2.5 parts of defibrinated
blood. This mixture is allowed to sediment for 30 minutes.
The supernatant, containing peripheral lymphocytes and the
granulocytes not removed in the fibrin clot, is removed and
centrifuged at 1500 rpm. The sedimented cells are separated
from the supernatant, resuspended, and recentrifuged at 800
rpm for five minutes in tubes measuring 11 by 0.3 cm. This
step deposits the red cells at the bottom, with the granulocytes adjacent, and leaves the lymphocytes in the supernatant, which is then removed.

This technic produces a lymphocyte suspension containing
an average of 50,000 cells per cubic millimeter. Lymphocytes
comprise 95-100 per cent of the white cells in the preparation, 99 per cent being viable by a trypan-blue exclusion test.
Erythrocyte contamination amounts to 20,000 cells per cubic
millimeter.

In performing the test, each prospective donor receives two
intradermal injections of 5×10^6 lymphocytes in the volar
aspect of the forearm, one from the prospective recipient and
the other from the unrelated control.

The resulting reactions observed are characterized by induration and erythema first observed at 24 hours and maximal
at 48 hours. These are believed to be on the basis of graft-
versus-host activity by the injected lymphocytes against antigens present in the host skin. Lymphocytes from the unrelated control injected into a donor panel consisting of a
sister, mother and unrelated volunteer, as illustrated, give a
maximal reaction in all three cases, indicating a high degree
of histocompatibility difference. In this figure the generally
closer histocompatibility relationship between close family
members is suggested by showing that lymphocytes from the
prospective recipient give a maximal reaction in the unrelated volunteer but smaller reactions in the sister and mother.
As illustrated, both the mother and sister show a lesser degree
of histocompatibility difference from the prospective recipient
than does the unrelated volunteer. Therefore, the mother or
sister would be a more suitable tissue donor than the unrelated volunteer.

successfully dealt with by the implantation technic, as indicated above, and quite a number of attempts to treat endocrine deficiencies, particularly hypo-parathyroidism, by this approach have been made. Although favorable metabolic effects have been reported to follow the use of both allogeneic[571] and xenogeneic parathyroid implants[572] no direct evidence of extended graft survival on histologic examination is available. Most authors doubt whether the grafted cells survive, but contend that their temporary presence may have altered the recipient in some favorable way. It is important to recognize, in work of this kind, that a patient's requirement for supportive treatment and his general clinical state can be misleading measures of parathyroid function.[573] A similar lack of unequivocal evidence of graft survival has yet to be overcome in cases in which primary vascularization of a block of pre-tracheal tissue containing thyroid and parathyroid glands has been achieved by joining appropriate vessels in the iliofemoral region, or elsewhere, with the vessels of the graft shortly after its removal from a stillborn fetal donor.[574,575]

Protection of grafted endocrine tissues from the attack of recipient cells by the use of the sheltering

---

FIGURE 16. *Runt Disease.*

A. *A typical runt.* A 21-day-old C57BL/6 animal which had received 5×10^6 DBA/1 adult spleen cells at birth. This animal has undergone the typical runting syndrome which is characterized by wasting, alopecia, generalized scaly dermatitis, diarrhea, and hepatosplenomegaly.

B. *Hepatosplenomegaly in runt disease.* Postmortem examination of the animal shown in *A,* revealing characteristic

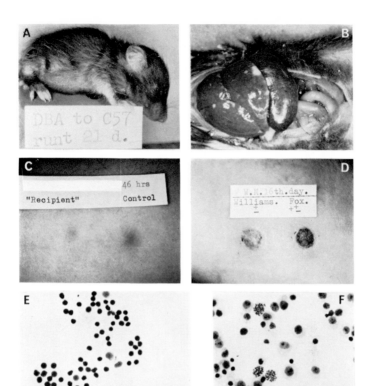

hepatosplenomegaly. On the surface of the liver can be seen the typical white patches found in runt disease, which on microscopic examination are found to be areas of coagulation necrosis.

Normal Lymphocyte Transfer Test

C. *Normal lymphocyte transfer test in man.* Two erythematous wheals with induration at 46 hours resulting from the intradermal injection of 5,000,000 lymphocytes obtained from the peripheral blood of 2 individuals. On the left is a + reaction which might be taken as selecting an appropriate donor-recipient combination as distinguished from the + + + reaction on the right.

D. *Prediction of skin graft rejection by the normal lymphocyte transfer test.* Two skin grafts on subject W.M. at day 16. W.M.'s lymphocytes had given a ± reaction when injected intradermally into subject Williams and a + ± reaction when injected into subject Fox. These reactions would indicate that Williams is a more compatible donor for W.M. than Fox. This prediction is borne out when skin grafts from Williams and Fox to W.M. are examined at day 16. The graft from Fox is fully rejected whereas that from Williams is still viable.

In vitro Histocompatibility Testing

E. *Culture of human lymphocytes from a single person.* In this preparation human lymphocytes have been grown in tissue culture for 7 days. During this time very little change in the cell morphology has taken place. Only a few large basophilic cells are present and no mitotic activity is evident.

F. *Culture of human lymphocytes stimulated with phytohemagglutinin.* In this preparation human lymphocytes have been grown in tissue culture for 3 days in the presence of phytohemagglutinin. In contrast to E at left, a high percentage of the lymphocytes have been stimulated by the phytohemagglutinin to develop into large basophilic cells with characteristic reticulated nuclei. A high degree of mitotic activity is demonstrated by chromosomal patterns present in several cells following treatment with vincaleucoblastine (Velban) for the terminal 4 hours of culture. This drug acts like colchicine and arrests mitosis. Similar changes occur in *mixed cultures* of human lymphocytes untreated with phytohemagglutinin, although the number of cells changed is smaller. The percentage of lymphocytes undergoing change in these *mixed cultures* may be a measure of the histocompatibility difference between the lymphocyte donors, thus forming the basis of an in vitro histocompatibility test system.

143

Millipore filter chamber is conceptually sound but has been disappointing in clinical trials.[576] A gradual decline in viability seems to occur in the specialized cells of functioning endocrine tissues when they are enclosed in Millipore filter chambers constructed with pores small enough to exclude the leukocytes of the recipient. This is probably on a nutritional basis and is doubtless hastened by the progressive occlusion of the pores with calcium salts and other debris that has been shown to occur.[577]

The present management of adrenal insufficiency is satisfactory enough to reduce the impetus of efforts to treat this condition with allogeneic tissue grafts. Of the many attempts so far made to do so none have been unquestionably successful.[578] Much the same situation applies to the treatment of diabetes with islet-cell tissue obtained in a variety of ways, a subject that has also received considerable attention from experimentalists.[579]

Skin grafts. Clinical attempts to perform allogeneic and even xenogeneic[123] skin grafts have been made for many years, usually in the treatment of extensive burns. The debilitated burned patient with large protein losses may occasionally accept allografts for a surprisingly long time.[580] Skin grafts constitute one of the few tissues in which current methods of long-term storage are quite satisfactory. The biologic obstacles that currently prevent the free use of other allogeneic tissues remain to be overcome. Indeed, it is generally agreed that skin is one of the "most demanding" tissues as a graft since small antigenic differences are usually sufficient to result in its rejection.

Bone marrow. Basic knowledge of the laws of

transplantation biology has provided an impetus for the use of hematopoietic tissue grafts in clinical medicine. A summary of the clinical literature is available in the review by Koller et al.[271] Infusions of isogeneic and stored autologous bone marrow have been used with some success to restore marrow function after lethal irradiation[581,582] and to prevent marrow failure after chemotherapy for malignant lesions.[583] Recently, 2 cases of idiopathic bone-marrow failure with recovery after infusion of isogeneic marrow from an identical twin have been reported.[584,585]

The use of allogeneic bone-marrow grafts has been under intensive study. Mathé and his co-workers[586] demonstrated the effectiveness of transient survival of infused allogeneic bone marrow after accidental exposure to whole-body irradiation. Four workers who had probably received 600 to 900 r in an explosion of a nuclear reactor in Vinca, Yugoslavia, reached an aplastic crisis and were given allogeneic marrow. Their condition improved rapidly, and there were indications that the grafted marrow survived and functioned for forty-five days, with later gradual replacement by host cells and recovery of the patients. Subsequently, a number of attempts were made to treat patients with leukemia with total-body irradiation followed by allogeneic bone marrow,[587,588] but long lasting remission of the disease or persistence of donor cells was not obtained. The problems involved in controlling undesirable immunologic activity in a situation in which the graft itself contains immunologically competent cells takes on the added requirement that potentially destructive reactions are mutually possible between graft and host (as pointed out above). Mathé et al.[589] underscored this possibility in a detailed description of cases in which they believed that the wasting syndrome had occurred in human beings, presumably on the basis of a graft-versus-host reaction. Leukemic patients who had received total-body irradiation and allogeneic bone marrow suffered severe diarrhea, weight loss, lymphoid aplasia and mild dermatitis and showed abnormal gamma globulins. The condition lasted for about thirty days, improving as donor erythrocytes disappeared. In another group of patients[590] a similar but much more severe form of this syndrome, with a rapidly fatal outcome, was observed. Recently, these authors[591] reported the first long-term hematopoietic chimera in man after allogeneic bone-marrow transplantation. In this case allogeneic bone marrow from multiple donors was administered to a leukemic patient after total-body irradiation. Studies of the resulting chimeric state, which had persisted for at least eight months at the time of their report, showed that the host probably had spontaneously selected the most compatible bone-marrow donor, as determined independently by blood-group determinations and histocompatibility studies, including leukocyte agglutinins and third-party skin-graft tests.[560]

It is clear, therefore, that once an effective program of histocompatibility testing is established, attention must be paid, in clinical allogeneic bone-marrow grafting, to antigens present in either member of the donor-recipient pair, but absent in the opposite individual, rather than merely to those present in the donor, but absent in the host, as is necessary with most tissues.

Lung. A few pulmonary transplants have recently been performed in a terminal effort to support the respiratory function of patients with bilateral pulmonary impairment. Those involved believed that the transplanted lungs functioned during the brief subsequent life of the patients.[592,593]

It is apparent that pulmonary transplantation is beset with special problems at the present time:

Source of donor tissue. Since cadaver tissue only should be used, the obstacles to a planned and orderly procedure are greater and the opportunity for careful selection of a donor, so important from several points of view, is less than with other transplants.

Assessment of rejection. Some degree of pulmonary edema is to be anticipated as a consequence of loss of lymphatic drainage and, conceivably, because of interruption of the normal nerve supply to the lung. In the face of this, and other changes that might be attributed to the operation itself, it may be difficult to appreciate the onset of rejection and to act promptly to combat it.

Control of infection. Since the transplant is exposed to inhaled organisms and, perhaps more important, since most conditions that might be treated by transplantation are likely to involve at least some superimposed infection, the danger of uncontrollable infection during the early stages of immunosuppressive drug treatment is likely to be high.

Nevertheless, in spite of these special difficulties, pulmonary transplantation appears to be potentially feasible.

Liver. Transplantation has been attempted clinically several times. Starzl and his colleagues,[594] in a group of 4 patients, 1 with biliary atresia and the others with primary hepatic cancers, achieved immediate survival in 3 cases. Serious difficulties were encountered with postoperative control of coagulation processes. An early marked rise in circulating fibrinolytic activity was followed, when this was reversed by the use of ε-aminocaproic acid treatment, by a hypercoagulable state. Clearly, the state of preservation of the donor organ is a matter of great importance to its early survival and satisfactory function. This factor was improved, in the cases reported, by a whole-body perfusion technic of the cadaver donors at hypothermic temperatures, begun immediately after death, to maintain the liver in as normal a state as possible during preparations for transplantation. One additional case has been reported,[595] also with early survival but subsequent rejection in spite of a full immunosuppressive drug program.

Spleen. Splenic allografts were performed in 5 cases by Starzl et al.[596] The spleens were transplanted heterotopically to the right iliac fossa. After operation in 1 patient, a child with hypogammaglobulinemia, evidence of splenic function was present at six weeks on immunosuppressive therapy as determined by a rise in serum gamma-globulin levels.

Heart. We are aware of one attempt at clinical cardiac transplantation. This involved the xenogeneic transplantation of a chimpanzee heart to a patient dying of heart failure in association with extensive occlusion of the coronary vessels.[597] The transplanted heart functioned well initially and sustained the patient for about one hour after the cardiac bypass was discontinued. It cannot be doubted that such a procedure is technically feasible, but it seems clear to us that further advances in these technics will not occur until they are joined by the power of greater fundamental knowledge.

Extremities. Autologous replantation of upper extremities has recently been performed with quite gratifying success in a number of cases, 2 of which have been particularly well documented.[598] The technical problems involved in allogeneic transfer of an extremity should be considerably less in view of the lack of diffuse damage to the variety of tissues involved, particularly the nerves. No success with allogeneic transplants has been reported.

Kidney. Clinical transplantation of the kidney, although still a distinctly experimental procedure, is far more advanced than that of any other organ This bilaterally symmetrical structure, the function of which can be readily and constantly measured, and which is endowed with a simple vascular pedicle, lends itself readily to transplantation. Although a number of attempts were made early in this century to treat renal failure by means of allografts or even xenografts[599] concerted efforts did not begin until mid-century. At first, kidneys obtained from cadavers were used and were usually placed in the groin.[600] No special treatment was given to modify the immunologic response, and little success resulted, except for one patient who survived with poor renal function for the impressive period of five months. Thereafter, a significant advance was made by Merrill and his colleagues[601] when they demonstrated that the rejection process would not occur in identical twins and that renal isografting could provide remarkably dramatic relief for renal failure. This turned the attention of many interested physicians to the fundamental experimental work in tissue immunogenetics that had been rapidly progressing during the previous decade and provided a new mutual stimulation between the clinic and the laboratory.

Subsequent progress by the pioneering group at the Peter Bent Brigham Hospital in Boston and by others, notably Hamburger and his colleagues at the Hôpital Necker in Paris, included a period during which whole-body irradiation was used to suppress recipient immune reactivity. Doses of irradiation in the lethal range proved to have too many side effects, and the establishment of stable allogeneic chimeras after bone-marrow infusions was found to be much more difficult in patients than in small animals. Smaller doses of irradiation, of approximately 400 r, were used to depress immunologic reactivity since they were safer, but this treatment has been abandoned by most groups in favor of various combinations of immunosuppressive drugs. The latter have allowed substantial improvement in the feasibility of caring for these very sick patients in that infection is somewhat less likely than after irradiation and the symptomatic side effects of irradiation can be avoided.

The development of renal transplantation has been the sole subject of a recent volume by Calne,[549] and its current status was fully discussed at a conference sponsored by the National Academy of Sciences–National Research Council in September, 1963.[359] A registry of patients treated in this way has been established with the support of the same sponsoring group under the direction of Dr. Joseph E. Murray,[602] who has reported the current total figures (as of March 15, 1964) of the world experience, in which a wide variety of different methods of management of patients have been used. A very brief extract of these figures is presented in Table 2.

TABLE 2. *Summarized Figures from Kidney Transplantation Registry (March 15, 1964).*[602]

Donor	Total Patients	Total Surviving at Present	Comment
Parents	99	42 (42%)	4 patients living >1 yr.
Siblings	65	31 (47%)	7 patients living >1yr.
Dizygotic twin	6	5 (83%)	3 patients living >1 yr.
Other blood relative	7	5 (71%)	No patients living >1 yr.
Nonrelated, living	66	11 (17%)	No patients living >1 yr.
Cadaver	99	17 (17%)	3 patients living >1 yr.
Monozygotic twin	32	24 (75%)	Longest survival now >8 yr. after operation
Totals	374	135 (36%)	

It can be seen from Table 2 that a large number of transplants have been performed within the past year, since most of the survivors have lived for less than one year since operation. More time is required before these figures will take on their full meaning. Although there is a distinctly better chance of survival by blind selection of close relatives rather than nonrelatives as donors, as might be expected, the fact that a number of patients are improved for some months, at least, with cadaver transplants is an interesting and noteworthy fact.

The data reported by Murray et al.[602] have been analyzed statistically by Dr. B. A. Barnes of the Massachusetts General Hospital in accordance with accepted practice in reporting end results in the treatment of cancer and other chronic diseases.[603] After a patient has received a renal allograft his original disease making transplantation necessary and the possible limitation of function of the allografted kidney reduce the patient's life expectancy below normal, and in each successive follow-up interval the compiled results reveal an ever increasing number of deaths and diminishing number of survivors. The survival data displayed in Table 3 are calculated from the reported data[602] of the Kidney Transplantation Registry and the method of derivation is explained in the accompanying legend.

The accumulated fractions surviving for the five groups of Table 3 have been plotted in Figure 17 with freehand curves drawn through the calculated points. The superiority of donors from a class including siblings and blood relatives is apparent for the allogeneic grafts. There is no significance after five years, possibly because of the small numbers of patients available for observation, between the survival of 53 per cent for the allogeneic grafts and 59 per cent for the isogeneic grafts. On the other hand, the standard error[604] of the 53 per cent survival of Group B is 6 per cent, indicating a significant difference from the one- to two-year results in Groups A and C, in which percentages of survivals are well outside a two-standard-deviation interval of the mean of Group B. The cause for the encouraging results in Group B as compared with Group A is not immediately evident. However, it may be that in practice a wider choice of donors has been explored in those clinical situations where a donor has been selected from siblings and blood relatives other than parents. Alternately, a strictly genetic explanation would emphasize the obligatory presence of half the genetic complement of the donor alien to the recipient when a parent is a donor. Finally, the effects of recent improvements in care of the patient with a renal allograft should be considered. Survival data derived from patients operated on within a year of the date of the report reveal that such patients benefited from the latest improvements in selection of donors, surgical technic, management of rejection crises, control of clinical infection, etc. For Group B the survival rate through the first year is now 63 per cent, and thus the data in Table 3 are conservative estimates of what may be accomplished even now with allogeneic renal grafts.

The fact that only 75 per cent of the recipients of isogeneic kidneys (from identical twins) are still living indicates that many causes of death in addition to orthodox transplant rejection may occur. The danger that glomerulonephritis will develop in a previously normal kidney from an identical twin donor appears now to be quite great and steadily increases with time.[605] Interestingly enough, this has likewise followed allogeneic transplantation, even though immunosuppressive drug therapy was simultaneously being administered in doses sufficient to control the rejection process. Although there is substantial evidence that graft-versus-host reactivity by a transplanted kidney is of little importance[228] it is of great interest that specific delayed hypersensitivity can be transferred between patients by kidney transplantation.[606]

It is clear from our experience, and that of others, that entirely normal renal function may con-

TABLE 3. *Survival Data of Human Kidney Allografts (derived from Tables III and IV of Murray et al.[602]).*

Group	Donor and Number	Total Patients	Results	Months					Years					
				0-1	1-3	3-6	6-12	1-2	2-3	3-4	4-5	5-6	6-7	7-8
A	Mother (67) or father (32)	99	q	35/96	8/52.5	2/31.5	3/17	5/7						
			F.S.	0.64	0.54	0.51	0.42	0.12						
B	Sister (30), brother (35), other blood relative (7), or dizygotic twin (6)	78	q	19/74.5	8/46.5	4/29.5	0/16.5	0/7.5	0/3	0/2	0/1.5	0/0.5		
			F.S.	0.75	0.62	0.53	0.53	0.53	0.53	0.53	0.53	0.53		
C	Spouse (9), living unrelated volunteer (25), or obligatory nephrectomy (32)	66	q	40/64.5	8/21.5	4/11	1/4.5	2/2						
			F.S.	0.38	0.24	0.15	0.12	0.00						
D	Cadaver (99)	99	q	64/98	14/30.5	3/11	1/4.5	0/1.5						
			F.S.	0.35	0.19	0.14	0.11	0.11						
E	Monozygotic twin (32)	32	q	3/32	0/28.5	1/27.5	0/25	1/22	0/16.5	0/12.5	0/9.5	2/7	0/3.5	0/2.5
			F.S.	0.91	0.91	0.87	0.87	0.83	0.83	0.83	0.83	0.59	0.59	0.59
	Total	374												

The Mortality Rate (q) for a given interval of the follow-up period equals the

$$\frac{\text{Number of patients dying in the interval}}{\text{The total number of patients alive at the start of the interval}}$$

The Fraction Surviving (F.S.) equals the product of the survival rates (1-q) of the previous intervals within each group. Thus, in Group A, for example, 99 patients received kidney transplants. Of these, 35 patients died during the first postoperative month and 6 surviving patients were operated upon so recently that at the date of the report their postoperative period of observation was less than one month in duration. On the average it is assumed that these 6 patients had a follow-up of one-half month, since the date of their operation in relation to the date of the report is presumably a matter of chance. Therefore, had they been observed for a full month, it is expected that deaths would have occurred at the same rate as in the larger group of cases observed throughout the month. Therefore, the mortality of the first month is

$$q* = \frac{35 + (6q/2)}{99} = \frac{35}{99 - (6/2)} = \frac{35}{96} = 0.36 \text{ or } 36 \text{ per cent}$$

The fraction of the 99 patients surviving this period is

$$p = 1-q = 0.64 \text{ or } 64 \text{ per cent}$$

Because of the above 35 deaths and 6 patients operated upon within a month of the date of the report, only 58 (99−35−6) patients were observed into the second interval of one to three months. Of these, 8 patients died and the 11 patients surviving were operated upon so recently that at the date of the report their period of observation was less than three months but longer than one month in duration. Calculated in the same way, the mortality of the one-to-three-month interval is

$$q* = \frac{8 + (11q/2)}{58} = \frac{8}{58 - (11/2)} = \frac{8}{52.5} = 0.15 \text{ or } 15 \text{ per cent}$$

The fraction of the 58 patients surviving this period is

$$p = 1-q = 0.85 \text{ or } 85 \text{ per cent}$$

The accumulated fraction surviving the first two intervals, i.e. from the date of operation through the third month, is the product of the previous fractions surviving within each period:

Accumulated Fraction Surviving (F.S.) = $0.64 \times 0.85 = 0.54$ or 54 per cent

The remaining mortality rates and accumulated fraction surviving have been similarly calculated *mutatis mutandis.*

_____

*The Mortality Rate (q) is determined by the formula

$$q = \frac{d + (W/2)}{o}, \text{ or } q = \frac{d}{o - (w/2)}$$

where q = mortality rate, d = number of patients dying in interval, w = number of patients observed through only part of interval, and o = number of patients entering interval.

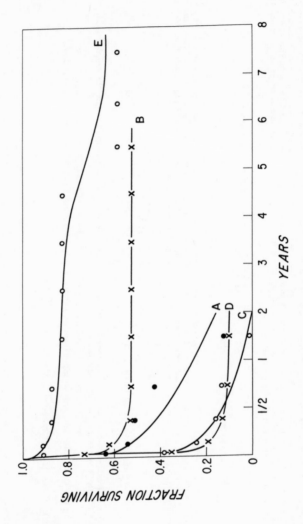

FIGURE 17. *Survival of Human Renal Allografts (see text).*

A. Parent donors B. Sibling donors C. Unrelated donors D. Cadaver donors
E. Monozygotic twins.

tinue for months in the face of a marked leukocytic infiltrate in the transplanted kidney. These cells, predominantly mononuclear, often insinuate themselves between the basement membrane and tubular epithelial cells in a manner reminiscent of the behavior of similar cells in the infiltrate seen in autoimmune thyroiditis.[607] Although the typical cellular reaction is usually observed, other forms of alteration have been found in kidney allografts. Some have described a very early (within a few hours) cessation of transplant function that has correlated with a fulminating hemorrhagic process in the kidney, giving a gross appearance resembling that which follows obstruction of the renal vein. No vascular obstruction has been reported in these cases, however, and the phenomenon has been attributed to the possible presence of serologic antibody as a consequence of prior chance sensitization of the recipient with antigens shared by the renal transplant.[608,609] Insufficient information is as yet available to allow full interpretation of these events with confidence.

Curious late pathological changes have also been described — for example, the late interstitial fibrosis and glomerular changes noted by Hamburger (as discussed by Antoine at the Kidney Homotransplantation Conference[359]). Porter et al.[610] have also recorded in detail the appearance of the vascular changes found earlier by Hume and his associates.[600] These consist of impressive intimal proliferation and rupture of the internal elastic lamina of renal arterioles. They believe that these changes lead to systemic arterial hypertension, but are not caused by it, and they suspect that they represent a variant of the rejection process.

The available experience has emphasized several points, in addition to those made elsewhere in this section: the incidence of prolonged survival is greater when living donors of the immediate family, siblings or parents, are used; active rejection of a transplanted kidney can be subject to striking reversal with immunosuppressive-drug treatment; 6-(1-methyl-4-nitro-5-imidazolyl)-thiopurine (Imuran) forms the basis of most drug treatment schedules currently in use (usefulness has also been found for actinomycin C, azaserine, cyclophosphamide and corticosteroids); and late failure of renal function, in association with a variety of pathological changes of as yet unknown cause, may occur.

Xenogeneic kidney transplants have also been performed in a number of cases.[611] In spite of the much greater immunologic differences involved it has been found that they can function surprisingly well. Rejection reactions can be modified by appropriate drug treatment, and survival of a patient with persisting function of a transplant beyond eight months has been reported. These unexpected results serve to emphasize the extent of present ignorance and to reinforce the need for fundamental investigation.

6

PROSPECTS FOR THE FUTURE

THE further development of tissue and organ transplantation as a practical method of treating disease must depend upon several parallel avenues of progress.

It is already apparent that many living organs, if in a sufficiently normal metabolic state, can be successfully transferred to their normal location in a needy recipient or to another more feasible, but equally effective, site. Technical advances are needed and will surely continue. Understanding of the complex immunologic events of tissue rejection is becoming rapidly more complete, and it now seems increasingly likely that it will be possible to control this destructive process safely in adults, perhaps by a combination of approaches. The fact that specific, long lived immunologic tolerance can be produced in adult laboratory animals is a hopeful finding of major potential value. The progress of methods of identifying transplantation antigens is also of profound importance since it may allow the choice of donor organs that do not differ in the more potent antigens, thus greatly reducing the force of the resultant immunologic reaction and the requirement for dangerous, and occasionally crippling, drug or radiation therapy in its suppression.

Eventually, full identification of the individual-specific antigens of a given organ must come. This can then be combined with long-term storage of tissues in a viable state, a technic that would add little by itself (without antigenic matching) to the percentage of success now possible. Organ storage is in its infancy, but again sufficient progress has already been made on which to found hope that this demanding problem will also yield, in due course, to continued investigation and will play its part in the future of "constructive surgery."

The ethical questions, now so pressing, that have been thrust upon us by progress in this area of medicine, as they have in others, will remain. The most difficult matter at present is the question of justifying the surgical invasion of an entirely normal person acting as an organ donor. Although a real danger to such a patient must be soberly acknowledged, it is reassuring to know that the continuing risk to a thirty-five-year-old person, otherwise normal, who has undergone nephrectomy is less than 2:1000 per five years from actuarial figures.[612] This source, taking a close relative, now offers the best chance of success in kidney transplantation. If the incidence of initial success of this treatment and the length of subsequent survival of transplant recipients continue to improve, guesswork will tend to be a lesser factor in the donor's decision to sacrifice a normal organ, and justification of the use of living donors, in very carefully selected cases, will become easier for the physician. Whether a sufficient supply of satisfactory organs for replacement is potentially available from recently deceased donors remains to be seen, but this source should become more appropriate as advancing knowledge begins to improve success with cadaver organs. It is to be expected that eventually stored organs, derived largely from cadaver donors, will serve as almost the entire source of supply.

REFERENCES

1. Medawar, P. B. Immunology of transplantation. *Harvey Lect.* (1956-1957) **52**:144-176, 1958.
2. Cannon, B., and Murray, J. E. Plastic surgery: tissue and organ homotransplantation. *New Eng. J. Med.* **255**:900-904, 1956.
3. Peer, L. A. *Transplantation of Tissues.* Vol. 2. *Skin, Cornea, Fat, Nerves, Teeth, Blood Vessels, Endocrine Glands, Organs, Peritoneum, Cancer Cells.* 675 pp. Baltimore: Williams & Wilkins, 1959.
4. Woodruff, M. F. A. *Transplantation of Tissues and Organs.* 816 pp. Springfield, Illinois: Thomas, 1960.
5. Gorer, P. A. Transplantese. *Ann. New York Acad. Sc.* **87**:604-607, 1960.
6. Gorer, P. A., Loutit, J. F., and Micklem, H. S. Proposed revisions of 'transplantese.' *Nature* (London) **189**:1024, 1961.
7. Medawar, P. B. Opening remarks. In *Ciba Foundation Symposium on Transplantation.* Edited by G. E. W. Wolstenholme and M. P. Cameron. 426 pp. Boston: Little, Brown, 1962. Pp. 1-5.
8. Snell, G. D. Terminology of tissue transplantation. *Transplantation* **2**:655-657, 1964.
9. Longmire, W. P., Cannon, J. A., and Weber, R. A. General surgical problems of tissue transplantation. In *Ciba Foundation Symposium on Preservation and Transplantation of Normal Tissues.* Edited by G. E. W. Wolstenholme, M. P. Cameron and J. Etherington. 236 pp. Boston: Little, Brown, 1954. Pp. 23-40.
10. Medawar, P. B. Behaviour and fate of skin autografts and skin homografts in rabbits (report to War Wounds Committee of Medical Research Council). *J. Anat.* **78**:176-199, 1944.
11. *Idem.* Second study of behaviour and fate of skin homografts in rabbits (report to War Wounds Committee of Medical Research Council). *J. Anat.* **79**:157-176, 1945.
12. Billingham, R. E., Brent, L., Brown, J. B., and Medawar, P. B. Time of onset and duration of transplantation immunity. *Transplantation Bull.* **6**:410-414, 1959.
13. Steinmuller, D., and Weiner, L. J. Evocation and persistence of transplantation immunity in rats. *Transplantation* **1**:97-106, 1963.
14. Billingham, R. E., Brent, L., Medawar, P. B., and Sparrow, E. M. Quantitative studies on tissue transplantation immunity. I. Survival times of skin homografts exchanged between members of different inbred strains of mice. *Proc. Roy. Soc., London, s. B.* **143**:43-58, 1954.
15. Zoticov, E. A., and Budik, V. M. Some peculiarities of survival time of skin homografts. *Ann. New York Acad. Sc.* **87**:16-74, 1960.

16. Martinez, C., Shapiro, F., and Good, R. A. Effect of amount of tissue grafted upon survival of skin homografts. *Proc. Soc. Exper. Biol. & Med.* **106**:476-480. 1961.
17. Matter, P., Chambler, K., Lewis, S. R., and Blocker, T. G., Jr. Relationship between survival time and size of homografts in rats. *Transplantation* **1**:157-164, 1963.
18. Scothorne, R. J. Studies on response of regional lymph node to skin homografts. *Ann. New York Acad. Sc.* **64**:1028-1039, 1957.
19. Mitchison, N. A. Passive transfer of transplantation immunity. *Proc. Roy. Soc., London, s. B.* **142**:72-87, 1954.
20. Mannick, J. A., Graziani, J. T., and Egdahl, R. H. Transplantation antigen recovered from cell culture medium. *Transplantation* **3**:321-333, 1964.
21. Algire, G. H., Weaver, J. M., and Prehn, R. T. Studies on tissue homotransplantation in mice, using diffusion-chamber methods. *Ann. New York Acad. Sc.* **64**:1009-1013, 1957.
22. Russell, P. S., and Sparrow, E. Unpublished data.
23. Fishman, M. Antibody formation *in vitro*. *J. Exper. Med.* **114**:837-856, 1961.
24. McKhann, C. F., and Berrian, J. H. Transplantation immunity: some properties of induction and expression. *Ann. Surg.* **150**:1025-1031, 1959.
25. Scothorne, R. J. Lymphatic repair and genesis of homograft immunity. *Ann. New York Acad. Sc.* **73**:673-675, 1958.
26. Converse, J. M., Ballantyne, D. L., Jr., and Woisky, J. Vascularization of skin homografts and transplantation immunity. *Ann. New York Acad. Sc.* **73**:693-697, 1958.
27. Russell, P. S. Endocrine grafting techniques. In *Transplantation of Tissues and Cells.* Edited by R. E. Billingham and W. K. Silvers. 149 pp. Philadelphia: Wistar Institute, 1961. Pp. 35-47.
28. Billingham, R. E., and Sparrow, E. M. Studies on nature of immunity to homologous grafted skin with special reference to use of pure epidermal grafts. *J. Exper. Biol.* **31**:16-39, 1954.
29. Weiner, J., Spiro, D., and Russell, P. S. Electron microscopic study of homograft reaction. *Am. J. Path.* **44**:319-347, 1964.
30. van Dooremaal, J. C. Die Entwickelung der in fremden Grund versetzten lebenden Gewebe. *Arch. f. Ophth.* **19**:359-373, 1873.
31. Greene, H. S. N. Compatibility and noncompatibility. *Ann. New York Acad. Sc.* **59**:311-321, 1955.
32. Browning, H. C., Sadler, W. A., and White, W. D. Isologous and homologous transplants of ovarian tissue in anterior eye chambers of intact and castrated male and female mice of inbred strains. *Am. J. Anat.* **105**:91-115, 1959.
33. Medawar, P. B., and Russell, P. S. Adrenal homografts in mice, with special reference to 'immunological adrenalectomy.' *Immunology* **1**:1-12, 1958.
34. Medawar. P. B. Immunity to homologous grafted skin. III. Fate of skin homografts transplanted to brain, to subcutaneous tissue, and to anterior chamber of eye. *Brit. J. Exper. Path.* **29**:58-69, 1948.
35. Woodruff, M. F. A., and Woodruff, H. G. Transplantation of normal tissue, with special reference to auto- and homotransplants of thyroid and spleen in anterior chamber of eye, and subcutaneously, in guinea pigs. *Philos. Tr. Roy. Soc., London, s. B.* **234**:559, 1950.
36. Billingham, R. E., and Boswell, T. Studies on problem of corneal homografts. *Proc. Roy. Soc., London, s. B.* **141**:392-406, 1953.
37. Maumenee, A. E. Influence of donor-recipient sensitization on corneal grafts. *Am. J. Ophth.* **34**:142-152, 1951.
38. Murphy, J. B.. and Sturm, E. Conditions determining transplantability of tissues in brain. *J. Exper. Med.* **38**:183-197, 1923.

References

References

39. Russell, P. S., and Wood, M. L. Unpublished data.
40. Billingham, R. E., and Silvers, W. K. Studies on cheek pouch skin homografts in Syrian hamster. In *Ciba Foundation Symposium on Transplantation*. Edited by G. E. W. Wolstenholme and M. P. Cameron. 426 pp. Boston: Little, Brown, 1962. Pp. 90-108.
41. Murphy, J. B. *Lymphocyte in Resistance to Tissue Grafting, Malignant Disease, and Tuberculous Infection*. 168 pp. New York: Rockefeller Institute for Medical Research, 1926. (No. 21, Monographs.)
42. Rapaport, F. T., and Converse, J. M. Immune response to multiple-set skin homografts: experimental study in man. *Ann. Surg.* **147**:273-280, 1958.
43. Gorer, P. A. Role of antibodies in immunity to transplanted leukaemia in mice. *J. Path. & Bact.* **54**:51-65, 1942.
44. *Idem*. Antibody response to tumor inoculation in mice: with special reference to partial antibodies. *Cancer Research* **7**:634-641, 1947.
45. Mitchison, N. A., and Dube, O. L. Studies on immunological response to foreign tumor transplants in mouse. II. Relation between hemagglutinating antibody and graft resistance in normal mouse and mice pretreated with tissue preparations. *J. Exper. Med.* **102**:179-197, 1955.
46. Billingham, R. E., and Brent, L. Further attempts to transfer transplantation immunity by means of serum. *Brit. J. Exper. Path.* **37**:566-569, 1956.
47. Lawrence, H. S., Rapaport, F. T., Converse, J. M., and Tillet, W. S. Homograft sensitivity in human beings. In *Ciba Foundation Symposium on Transplantation*. Edited by G. E. W. Wolstenholme and M. P. Cameron. 426 pp. Boston: Little, Brown, 1962. Pp. 271-281.
48. Brent, L., Brown, J., and Medawar, P. B. Skin transplantation immunity in relation to hypersensitivity. *Lancet* **2**:561-564, 1958.
49. *Idem*. Quantitative studies on tissue transplantation immunity. VI. Hypersensitivity reactions associated with rejection of homografts. *Proc. Roy. Soc., London, s. B.* **156**:187-209, 1962.
50. Dvorak, H. F., and Waksman, B. H. Primary immunization of lymph node cells in millipore chambers by exposure to homograft antigen. *J. Exper. Med.* **116**:1-16, 1962.
51. Janković, B. D., and Dvorak, H. F. Enzymatic inactivation of immunologically competent lymph node cells in "transfer reaction." *J. Immunol.* **89**:571-581, 1962.
52. Merrill, J. P., Friedman, E. A., Wilson, R. E., and Marshall, D. C. Production of "delayed type" cutaneous hypersensitivity to human donor leukocytes as result of rejection of skin homografts. *J. Clin. Investigation* **40**:631-635, 1961.
53. Weaver, J. M., Algire. G. H., and Prehn, R. T. Growth of cells *in vivo* in diffusion chambers. II. Role of cells in destruction of homografts in mice. *J. Nat. Cancer Inst.* **15**:1737-1767, 1955.
54. Conference on Cell-Bound Antibodies, Washington, D. C., 1963. *Cell-Bound Antibodies: Conference of the National Academy of Sciences-National Research Council, held May 10 1963: Sponsored by Committee on Tissue Transplantation of the Division of Medical Sciences, National Academy of Sciences-National Research Council*. Edited by D. B. Amos and H. Koprowski. 134 pp. Philadelphia: Wistar Institute, 1963.
55. Lawrence, H. S.[54] Pp. 3-6.
56. McCluskey, R. T., Benacerraf, B., and McCluskey, J. W. Studies on specificity of cellular infiltrate in delayed hypersensitivity reactions. *J. Immunol.* **90**:466-477, 1963.

57. Najarian, J. S., and Feldman, J. D. Passive transfer of tuberculin sensitivity by tritiated thymidine-labeled lymphoid cells. *J. Exper. Med.* **114**:779-790, 1961.
58. Prendergast, R. A. Cellular specificity in homograft reaction. *J. Exper. Med.* **119**:377-387, 1964.
59. Stetson, C. A. Role of humoral antibody in homograft reaction. In *Advances in Immunol.* **3**:97-130, 1963.
60. Gorer, P. A., and Mikulska, Z. B. Antibody response to tumor inoculation: improved methods of antibody detection. *Cancer Research* **14**:651-655, 1954.
61. Amos, D. B. Agglutination of mouse leucocytes by iso-immune sera. *Brit. J. Exper. Path.* **34**:455-470, 1953.
62. Gorer, P. A., and O'Gorman, P. Cytotoxic activity of isoantibodies in mice. *Transplantation Bull.* **3**:142, 1956.
63. Reif, A. E., and Norris, H. J. System for quantitative determination of cytotoxic activity of antisera to ascites tumor cells. *Cancer Research* **20**:1235-1244, 1960.
64. Terasaki, P. I., Bold, E. J., Cannon, J. A., and Longmire, W. P., Jr. Antibody response to homografts. VI. *In vitro* cytotoxins produced by skin homografts in rabbits. *Proc. Soc. Exper. Biol. & Med.* **106**:133-136, 1961.
65. Palm, J. Current status of blood groups in rats. *Ann. New York Acad. Sc.* **97**:57-68, 1962.
66. Hancock, D. M., and Mullan, F. A. Appearance of hemagglutinins after homografting in rabbits. *Ann. New York Acad. Sc.* **99**:534-541, 1962.
67. Kapitchnikov, M. M., Ballantyne, D. L., Jr., and Stetson, C. A. Immunological reactions to skin homotransplantation in rabbits and rats. *Ann. New York Acad. Sc.* **99**:497-503, 1962.
68. Swisher, S. N., Young, L. E., and Trabold, N. *In vitro* and *in vivo* studies of behavior of canine erythrocyte-isoantibody systems. *Ann. New York Acad. Sc.* **97**:15-25, 1962.
69. Walford, R. L., Anderson, R. E., Carter, P. K., and Mihajlovic, F. Leukocyte antibodies in inbred strains of guinea pigs following first- and second-set skin homografts. *J. Immunol.* **89**:427-433, 1962.
70. Walford, R. L., Carter, P. K., and Anderson, R. E. Leukocyte antibodies following skin homografting in human. *Transplantation Bull.* **29**:16-18, 1962.
71. Hildemann, W. H. Immunogenetic studies of amphibians and reptiles. *Ann. New York Acad. Sc.* **97**:139-152, 1962.
72. Ridgway, G. J. Demonstration of blood groups in trout and salmon by isoimmunization. *Ann. New York Acad. Sc.* **97**:111-115, 1962.
73. Gorer, P. A., Mikulska, Z. B., and O'Gorman, P. Time of appearance of isoantibodies during homograft response to mouse tumours. *Immunology* **2**:211-218, 1959.
74. Jensen, E., and Stetson, C. A., Jr. Humoral aspects of immune response to homografts. II. Relationship between hemagglutinating and cytotoxic activities of certain isoimmune sera. *J. Exper. Med.* **113**:785-794, 1961.
75. Terasaki, P. I. Antibody response to homografts. II. Preliminary studies of time of appearance of lymphoagglutinins upon homografting. *Am. Surgeon* **25**:896-899, 1959.
76. Stetson, C. A., and Jensen, E. Humoral aspects of immune response to homografts. *Ann. New York Acad. Sc.* **87**:249-257, 1960.
77. Medawar, P. B. Immunity to homologous grafted skin. II. Relationship between antigens of blood and skin. *Brit. J. Exper. Path.* **27**:15-24, 1946.
78. *Idem.* Tests by tissue culture methods on nature of immunity to transplanted skin. *Quart. J. Microscopic Soc.* **89**:239, 1948.

79. Allgöwer, M., Blocker, T. G., Jr., and Engley, B. W. D. Some immunological aspects of auto- and homografts in rabbits, tested by *in vivo* and *in vitro* techniques. *Plast. & Reconstruct. Surg.* **9**: 1-21, 1952.

80. Algire, G. H. Vascular reactions of normal and malignant tissues *in vivo*. VII. Observations on vascular reactions in destruction of tumor homografts. *J. Nat. Cancer Inst.* **15**:483-491, 1954.

81. Billingham, R. E., Brent, L., and Medawar, P. B. Quantitative studies on tissue transplantation immunity. II. Origin, strength and duration of actively and adoptively acquired immunity. *Proc. Roy. Soc., London, s. B.* **143**:58-80, 1954.

82. Wakefield, J. D., and Amos, D. B. Effect of iso-antibody on ascites cells grown in diffusion chambers. *Proc. Am. A. Cancer Research* **2**:354, 1958.

83. Gorer, P. A., and Boyse, E. A. Some reactions observed with transplanted reticulo-endothelial cells in mice. In *Symposium on Biological Problems of Grafting: A symposium sponsored by the Comm. administrative de Liège and the Council for International Organizations of Medical Sciences.* Edited by F. Albert and P. B. Medawar. 453 pp. Oxford: Blackwell, 1959. Pp. 192-204.

84. Gabourel, J. D. Cell culture *in vivo*. II. Behavior of L-fibroblasts in diffusion chambers in resistant hosts. *Cancer Research* **21**:506-509, 1961.

85. Algire, G. H. Growth inhibition of homografts of plasma-cell neoplasm in cell-impenetrable diffusion chambers placed in hyper-immunized mice. *J. Nat. Cancer Inst.* **23**:435-439, 1959.

86. Gorer, P. A. Some recent work on tumor immunity. In *Advances in Cancer Research* **4**:149-186, 1956.

87. Gorer, P. A., and Kaliss, N. Effect of isoantibodies *in vivo* on three different transplantable neoplasms in mice. *Cancer Research* **19**:824-830, 1959.

88. Harris, T. N., Harris, S., and Farber, M. B. Studies on transfer of lymph node cells. XI. Effect on anti-Shigella agglutinin titers of recipient rabbits of prior injection of leucocytes from donor animals. *J. Exper. Med.* **108**:21-36, 1958.

89. *Idem.* Suppression of transferred lymph node cells by rabbit-antirabbit leukocyte serum. *J. Immunol.* **87**:536-547, 1961.

90. Harris, T. N., Ogburn, C. A., Harris, S., and Farber, M. B. Preparation by elution from specific aggregates of isoantibody causing rejection of transferred rabbit lymph node cells. *Transplantation* **1**:261-269, 1963.

91. Siskind, G. E., and Thomas, L. Studies on runting syndrome in newborn mice. In *Symposium on Biological Problems of Grafting: A symposium sponsored by the Comm. administrative de Liège and the Council for International Organizations of Medical Sciences.* Edited by F. Albert and P. B. Medawar. 453 pp. Oxford: Blackwell, 1959. Pp. 178-186.

92. Russell, P. S. Modification of runt disease in mice by various means. In *Ciba Foundation Symposium on Transplantation.* Edited by G. E. W. Wolstenholme and M. P. Cameron. 426 pp. Boston: Little, Brown, 1962. Pp. 350-378.

93. Stetson, C. A., Jr., and Demopoulos, R. Reactions of skin homografts with specific immune sera. *Ann. New York Acad. Sc.* **73**: 687-692, 1958.

94. Steinmuller, D. Passive transfer of immunity to skin homografts in rats. *Ann. New York Acad. Sc.* **99**:629-644, 1962.

95. Schinkel, P. G., and Ferguson, K. A. Skin transplantation in fetal lamb. *Australian J. Exper. Biol. & M. Sc.* **6**:533-546, 1953.

96. Silverstein, A. M. Ontogeny of immune response: development of immunologic responses by fetus has interesting pathobiologic implication. *Science* **144**:1423-1428, 1964.

97. Silverstein, A. M., Prendergast, R. A., and Kraner, K. L. Fetal response to antigenic stimulus. IV. Rejection of skin homografts by fetal lamb. *J. Exper. Med.* **119**:955-964, 1964.

98. *Idem.* Homograft rejection in fetal lamb: role of circulating antibody. *Science* **142**:1172, 1963.

99. Guiney, E. J., Austen, K. F., and Russell, P. S. Measurement of serum complement during homograft rejection in man and rat. *Proc. Soc. Exper. Biol. & Med.* **115**:1113-1117, 1964.

100. Boyden, S. V., and Sorkin, E. Adsorption of antigen by spleen cells previously treated with antiserum *in vitro*. *Immunology* **3**: 272-283, 1960.

101. *Idem.* Adsorption of antibody and antigen by spleen cells *in vitro*: some further experiments. *Immunology* **4**:244-252, 1961.

102. Koprowski, H., and Fernandes, M. V. Autosensitization reaction *in vitro*. contactual agglutination of sensitized lymph node cells in brain tissue culture accompanied by destruction of glial elements. *J. Exper. Med.* **116**:467-476, 1962.

103. Warnatz, H., and Scheiffarth, F. Cellular fixed antibodies in transplantation immunity. *Nature* (London) **201**:408, 1964.

104. Freedman, S. O., Turcotte, R., Fish, A. J., and Sehon, A. H. *In vitro* detection of "cell-fixed" hemagglutinating antibodies to tuberculin purified protein derivative (PPD) in humans. *J. Immunol.* **90**:52-59, 1963.

105. Lawrence, H. S. Some biological and immunological properties of transfer factor. In *Ciba Foundation Symposium on Cellular Aspects of Immunity.* Edited by G. E. W. Wolstenholme and M. O'Connor. 474 pp. Boston: Little, Brown, 1960. Pp. 243-271.

106. *Idem.* Transfer in humans of delayed skin sensitivity to streptococcal M substance and to tuberculin with disrupted leucocytes. *J. Clin. Investigation* **34**:219-230, 1955.

107. Lawrence, H. S., and Pappenheimer, A. M., Jr. Transfer of delayed hypersensitivity to diphtheria toxin in man. *J. Exper. Med.* **104**:321-336, 1956.

108. Rapaport, F. T., Lawrence, H. S., Millar, J. W., Pappagianis, D., and Smith, C. E. Transfer of delayed hypersensitivity to coccidioidin in man. *J. Immunol.* **84**:358-367, 1960.

109. Freedman, S. O., Fisher, J. P., and Cooke, R. A. Study of leukocytic antibodies in allergic patients. *J. Allergy* **28**:501-513, 1957.

110. Maurer, P. H. Immunologic studies with ethylene oxide-treated human serum. *J. Exper. Med.* **113**:1029-1039, 1961.

111. Turk, J. L. Passive transfer of contact sensitivity of picryl chloride in guinea pigs, with subcellular material. *Nature* (London) **191**:915, 1961.

112. Powell, A. E., Ray, O., Whitenack, D., Hubay, C. A., and Holden, W. D. Skin reaction in guinea pig homograft donors with cell-free substance from recipient lymph nodes. *Nature* (London) **193**:1198, 1962.

113. Powell, A. E., Ray, O., Hubay, C. A., and Holden, W. D. Induced rejection of guinea pig skin homografts by partially purified transfer factor. *J. Immunol.* **92**:73-81, 1964.

114. Najarian, J. S., and Feldman, J. D. Passive transfer of transplantation immunity. I. Tritiated lymphoid cells. II. Lymphoid cells in millipore chambers. *J. Exper. Med.* **115**:1083-1093, 1962.

115. *Idem.* Passive transfer of transplantation immunity. III. Inbred guinea pigs. *J. Exper. Med.* **117**:449-456, 1963.

116. Kretschmer, R. R., and Pérez-Tamayo, R. Role of humoral antibodies in rejection of skin homografts in rabbits. II. Passive transfer of transplantation immunity by sensitized lymph node cells within diffusion chambers. *J. Exper. Med.* **116**:879-896, 1962.

117. Najarian, J. S., and Feldman, J. D. Observations on passive transfer of transplantation immunity and delayed hypersensitivity with lymphoid cells in millipore chambers. *Transplantation* **1**: 495-501, 1963.
118. Billingham, R. E., Silvers, W. K., and Wilson, D. B. Further studies on adoptive transfer of sensitivity to skin homografts. *J. Exper. Med.* **118**:397-420, 1963.
119. Mannick, J. A., and Egdahl, R. H. Ribonucleic acid in "transformation" of lymphoid cells. *Science* **137**:976, 1962.
120. Brent, L., Brown, J., and Medawar, P. B. Skin transplantation immunity in relation to hypersensitivity reactions of delayed type. In Symposium on Biological Problems of Grafting. *Biological Problems of Grafting: A symposium sponsored by the Comm. administrative de Liège and the Council for International Organizations of Medical Sciences.* Edited by F. Albert and P. B. Medawar. 453 pp. Oxford: Blackwell, 1959. Pp. 64-78.
121. Mannick, J. A. Transfer of "adoptive" immunity to skin homografts by RNA. *Federation Proc.* **23**:344, 1964.
122. Trakatellis, A. C., Axelrod, A. E., Montjar, M., and Lamy, F. Induction of immune tolerance with ribosomes and ribonucleic acid, extracts in newborn mice. *Nature* (London) **202**:154-157, 1964.
123. Gibson, T. Zoografting: curious chapter in history of plastic surgery. *Brit. J. Plast. Surg.* **8**:234-242, 1955.
124. Brocades Zaalberg, A., Vos, O., and van Bekkum, D. W. Surviving rat skin grafts in mice. *Nature* (London) **180**:238, 1957.
125. Hašek, M, Lengerová, A., and Hraba, T. Transplantation immunity and tolerance. *Advances in Immunol.* **1**:1-66, 1961.
126. Egdahl, R. H., Roller, F. R., Swanson, R. L., and Varco, R. L. Acquired tolerance to homografts and heterografts in rat. *Ann. New York Acad. Sc.* **73**:842-847, 1958.
127. Rowley, D. A. Formation of circulating antibody in splenectomized human being following intravenous injection of heterologous erythrocytes. *J. Immunol.* **65**:515-521, 1950.
128. Krohn, P. L. Influence of spleen on homograft reaction. *Transplantation Bull.* **1**:21, 1953.
129. Prehn, R. T. Immunity inhibiting role of spleen and effect of dosage and route of antigen administration in homograft reaction. In Symposium on Biological Problems of Grafting. *Biological Problems of Grafting: A symposium sponsored by the Comm. administrative de Liège and the Council for International Organizations of Medical Sciences.* Edited by F. Albert and P. B. Medawar. 453 pp. Oxford: Blackwell, 1959. Pp. 163-173.
130. McKhann, C. F. Transplantation studies of strong and weak histocompatibility barriers in mice. I. Immunization. *Transplantation* **2**:613-619, 1964.
131. McKenna, J. M., and Zweifach, B. Reticulo-endothelial system in relation to drum shock. *Am. J. Physiol.* **187**:263-268, 1956.
132. Beeson, P. B. Tolerance to bacterial pyrogens. II. Rôle of reticulo-endothelial system. *J. Exper. Med.* **86**:39-44, 1947.
133. Biozzi, G., Halpern, B. N., and Stiffel, C. Council for International Organizations of Medical Sciences. *Physiopathology of the Reticulo-Endothelial System: A symposium, Paris, 1955.* Edited under direction of B. N. Halpern, by B. Benacerraf and J. F. Delafresnaye. 317 pp. Oxford: Blackwell, 1957. P. 204.
134. Hektoen, L., and Corper, H. J. Influence of thorium X on antibody formation. *J. Infect. Dis.* **26**:330-335, 1920.
135. Thorbecke, G. J., and Benacerraf, B. Reticulo-endothelial system and immunological phenomena. *Progr. in Allergy* **6**:559-598, 1962.

136. Cutler, J. L. Enhancement of hemolysin production in rat by Zymosan. *J. Immunol.* **84**:416-419, 1960.
137. Halpern, B. N. Role and function of reticulo-endothelial system in immunological processes. *J. Pharm. & Pharmacol.* **11**:321-338, 1959.
138. Speirs, R. S. Theory of antibody formation involving eosinophils and reticuloendothelial cells. *Nature* (London) **181**:681, 1958.
139. Fishman, M. Antibody formation in tissue culture. *Nature* (London) **183**:1200, 1959.
140. Brent, L., and Medawar, P. B. Quantitative studies on tissue transplantation immunity. V. Role of antiserum in enhancement and desensitization. *Proc. Roy. Soc., London, s. B.* **155**:392-416, 1962.
141. Medawar, P. B. Use of antigenic tissue extracts to weaken immunological reaction against skin homografts in mice. *Transplantation* **1**:21-38, 1963.
142. Fisher, B., and Fisher, E. R. Tissue transplantation and reticuloendothelial system. I. Effect of skin grafts in normal animals. *Transplantation* **2**:228-234, 1964.
143. Gowans, J. L., McGregor, D. D., and Cowen, D. M. Initiation of immune responses by small lymphocytes. *Nature* (London) **196**:651-655, 1962.
144. Gowans, J. L., and McGregor, D. D. In International Symposium on Immunopathology. 3d, La Jolla, California, 1962. *The Origin of Antibody-Forming Cells.* Edited by T. Graber. New York: Grune, 1963. Pp. 89-98.
145. McGregor, D. D., and Gowans, J. L. Antibody response of rats depleted of lymphocytes by chronic drainage from thoracic duct. *J. Exper. Med.* **117**:303-320, 1962.
146. McGregor, D. D., and Gowans, J. L. Survival of homografts of skin in rats depleted of lymphocytes by chronic drainage from thoracic duct. *Lancet* **1**:629-632, 1964.
147. Gowans, J. L., and Knight, E. J. Route of re-circulation of lymphocytes in rat. *Proc. Roy. Soc., London, s. B.* **159**:257-282, 1964.
148. Woodruff, M. F. A., and Anderson, N. A. Effect of lymphocyte depletion by thoracic duct fistula and administration of antilymphocytic serum on survival of skin homografts in rats. *Nature* (London) **200**:702, 1963.
149. Sacks, J. H., Filippone, D. R., and Hume, D. M. Studies of immune destruction of lymphoid tissue. I. Lymphocytotoxic effect of rabbit-anti-rat lymphocyte antiserum. *Transplantation* **2**:60-74, 1964.
150. Humphrey, J. H. In Czechoslovak Academy of Sciences, Institute of Biology, Immunological Division. *Mechanisms of Antibody Formation: Proceedings of a symposium held in Prague, May 27-31, 1959.* Edited by M. Holub and J. Jarošková. 385 pp. Prague: The Division, 1960. P. 180.
151. Wilhelm, R. E., Fisher, J. P., and Cooke, R. A. Experimental depletion of mononuclear cells for purpose of investigating reactions of allergic contact type. *J. Allergy* **29**:493-501, 1958.
152. Chew, W. B., Stephens, D. J., and Lawrence, J. S. Antileucocytic serum. *J. Immunol.* **30**:301-318, 1936.
153. Cruickshank, A. H. Anti-lymphocytic serum. *Brit. J. Exper. Path.* **22**:126-136, 1941.
154. Woodruff, M. F. A., and Forman, B. Effect of anti-lymphocytic serum on suspensions of lymphocytes *in vitro*. *Nature* (London) **168**:35, 1951.
155. Gray, J. G., Monaco, A. P., and Russell, P. S. Heterologous mouse anti-lymphocyte serum to prolong skin homografts. *S. Forum* **15**:142-144, 1964.

156. Woodruff, M. F. A. Personal communication.
157. Waksman, B. H., Arbouys, S., and Arnason, B. G. Use of specific "lymphocyte" antisera to inhibit hypersensitive reactions of "delayed" type. *J. Exper. Med.* **114**:997-1022, 1961.
158. Waksman, B. H., and Arbouys, S. Use of specific "lymphocyte" antisera to inhibit hypersensitive reactions of "delayed" type. In Czechoslovak Academy of Sciences, Institute of Biology, Immunological Division. *Mechanisms of Antibody Formation: Proceedings of a symposium held in Prague, May 27-31, 1959.* Edited by M. Holub and J. Jaroškova. 385 pp. Prague: The Division, 1960. Pp. 165-178.
159. Woodruff, M. F. A., and Anderson, N. A. The effect of lymphocyte depletion by thoracic duct fistula and administration of antilymphocytic serum on the survival of skin homografts in rats. *Ann. New York Acad. Sc.* **120**:119-128, 1964.
160. Winchell, H. S., Pollycove, M., Anderson, A. C., and Lawrence, J. H. Relatively selective beta irradiation of lymphatic structures in dog using Y90-DTPA. *Blood* **23**:321-336, 1964.
161. Barnes, B. A., Brownell, G. L., and Flax, M. H. Irradiation of the blood. Method for reducing lymphocytes in blood and spleen. *Science* **145**:1188-1189, 1964.
162. Medawar, P. B. Immunological tolerance: phenomenon of tolerance provides testing ground for theories of immune response. *Science* **133**:303-306, 1961.
163. Owen, R. D. Immunogenetic consequences of vascular anastomoses between bovine twins. *Science* **102**:400, 1945.
164. Owen, R. D., Davis, H. P., and Morgan, R. F. Quintuplet calves and erythrocyte mosaicism. *J. Hered.* **37**:290-297, 1946.
165. Stone, W., Stormont, C., and Irwin, M. R. Blood typing as means of differentiating potentially fertile from non-fertile heifer born twin with bull. *J. Animal Sc.* **11**:744, 1952.
166. Stormont, C., Weir, W. C., and Lane, L. L. Erythrocyte mosaicism in pair of sheep twins. *Science* **118**:695, 1953.
167. Dunsford, I., et al. Human blood-group chimera. *Brit. M. J.* **2**:81, 1953.
168. Booth, P. B., et al. Blood chimerism in pair of twins. *Brit. M. J.* **1**:1456-1458, 1957.
169. Nicholas, J. W., Jenkins, W. J., and Marsh, W. L. Human blood chimeras: study of surviving twins. *Brit. M. J.* **1**:1458-1460, 1957.
170. Burnet, F. M., and Fenner, F. Genetics and immunology. *Heredity* **2**:289, 1948.
171. *Idem. Production of Antibodies.* Second edition. 142 pp. Melbourne: Macmillan, 1949.
172. Anderson, D., Billingham, R. E., Lampkin, G. H., and Medawar, P. B. Use of skin grafting to distinguish between monozygotic and dizygotic twins in cattle. *Heredity* **5**:379-398, 1951.
173. Billingham, R. E., Lampkin, G. H., Medawar, P. B., and Williams, H. L. L. Tolerance to homografts, twin diagnosis and freemartin condition in cattle. *Heredity* **6**:201-212, 1952.
174. Billingham, R. E., Brent, L., and Medawar, P. B. "Actively acquired tolerance" of foreign cells. *Nature* (London) **172**:603-606, 1953.
175. *Idem.* Acquired tolerance of skin homografts. *Ann. New York Acad. Sc.* **59**:409-416, 1955.
176. Hašek, M. Parabiosis in birds during embryonic development. *Čsl. Biol.* **2**:29-31, 1953.
177. *Idem.* Vegetative hybrization of animals by means of junction of blood circulation during embryonic development. *Čsl. Biol.* **2**:267-282, 1953.

178. *Idem.* Manifestations of vegetative relationship in adaptation of higher animals to heterogeneous antigens. *Čsl. Biol.* **3**:344-351, 1954.
179. Billingham, R. E., and Brent, L. Acquired tolerance of foreign cells in newborn animals. *Proc. Roy. Soc., London, s. B.* **146**: 78-90, 1957.
180. Billingham, R. E., Brent, L., and Medawar, P. B. Quantitative studies on tissue transplantation immunity. III. Actively acquired tolerance. *Philos. Tr. Rcy. Soc., London* **239**:357-414, 1956.
181. Billingham, R. E. Studies on reaction of injected homologous lymphoid tissue cells against host. *Transplantation Bull.* **5**: 80, 1958.
182. Smith, R. T., and Bridges, R. A. Immunological unresponsiveness in rabbits produced by neonatal injection of defined antigens. *J. Exper. Med.* **108**:227-250, 1958.
183. Wolfe, H. R., Tempelis, C., Mueller, A., and Reibel, S. Precipitin production in chickens. XVII. Effect of massive injections of bovine serum albumin at hatching on subsequent antibody production. *J. Immunol.* **79**:147-153, 1957.
184. Terres, G., and Hughes, W. L. Acquired partial tolerance in mice to crystalline bovine serum albumin. *Federation Proc.* **17**: 536, 1958.
185. Mitchison, N. A. Blood transfusion in fowl: example of immunological tolerance requiring persistence of antigen. In Symposium on Biological Problems of Grafting. *Biological Problems of Grafting: A symposium sponsored by the Comm. administrative de Liège and the Council for International Organizations of Medical Sciences.* Edited by F. Albert and P. B. Medawar. 453 pp. Oxford: Blackwell, 1959. Pp. 239-259.
186. Medawar, P. B. Introduction. In Symposium on Mechanisms of Immunological Tolerance, Liblice, 1961. *Mechanisms of Immunological Tolerance: Proceedings of a symposium held at Liblice near Prague, Nov. 8-10, 1961.* Edited by M. Hašek et al. 544 pp. New York: Academic Press, 1963. (Symposia CSAV, sv5). Pp. 17-20.
187. Martinez, C., Shapiro, F., Kelman, H., Onstad, T., and Good, R. A. Tolerance of F_1 hybrid skin homografts in parent strain induced by parabiosis. *Proc. Soc. Exper. Biol. & Med.* **103**:266-269, 1960.
188. Rubin, B. A. Tolerance to skin homografts of adult mice after parabiosis. *Nature* (London) **184**:205, 1959.
189. Jensen, E., and Simonsen, M. Induced tolerance after parabiosis: apparent facilitation of tolerance by simultaneous graft-versus-host reaction. *Ann. New York Acad. Sc.* **99**:657-662, 1962.
190. Mariani, T., Martinez, C., Smith, J. M., and Good, R. A. Induction of immunological tolerance to male skin isografts in female mice subsequent to neonatal period. *Proc. Soc. Exper. Biol. & Med.* **101**:596-599, 1959.
191. Shapiro, F., Martinez, C., and Good, R. A. Homologous skin transplantation from F_1 hybrid mice to parent strains. *Proc. Soc. Exper. Biol. & Med.* **101**:94-97, 1959.
192. Shapiro, F., Martinez, C., Smith, J. M., and Good, R. A. Tolerance of skin homografts induced in adult mice by multiple injections of homologous spleen cells. *Proc. Soc. Exper. Biol. & Med.* **106**:472-475, 1961.
193. McKhann, C. F. Transplantation studies of strong and weak histocompatibility barriers in mice. II. Tolerance. *Transplantation* **2**:620-626, 1964.
194. Brent, L., and Gowland, G. Induction of tolerance of skin homografts in immunologically competent mice. *Nature* (London) **196**:1298-1301, 1962.

195. Brent, L., and Gowland, G. Quantitative analysis of tolerance induction in mice. In Symposium on Mechanisms of Immunological Tolerance, Liblice, 1961. *Mechanisms of Immunological Tolerance: Proceedings of a symposium held at Liblice near Prague, Nov. 8-10, 1961.* Edited by M. Hašek et al. 544 pp. New York: Academic Press, 1963. (Symposia CSAV, sv5). Pp. 237-243.

196. *Idem. Conceptional Advances in Immunology and Oncology: A collection of papers.* 557 pp. New York: Harper & Row, 1963. P. 355.

197. Howard, J. G., and Michie, D. Induction of transplantation immunity in newborn mouse. *Transplantation Bull.* **29**:1-6, 1962.

198. *Idem.* Specific and non-specific aspects of neonatal vaccination against graft-versus-host reaction. *Transplantation* **1**:377-384, 1963.

199. Howard, J. G., Michie, D., and Woodruff, M. F. A. Transplantation tolerance and immunity in relation to age. In *Ciba Foundation Symposium on Transplantation.* Edited by G. E. W. Wolstenholme and M. P. Cameron. 426 pp. Boston: Little, Brown, 1962. Pp. 138-153.

200. Brent, L., and Gowland, G. Immunological competence of newborn mice. *Transplantation* **1**:372-376, 1963.

201. Uhr, J. W. Development of delayed-type hypersensitivity in guinea pig embryos. *Nature* (London) **187**:957-959, 1960.

202. Uhr, J. W., Dancis, J., and Neumann, C. G. Delayed-type hypersensitivity in premature neonatal humans. *Nature* (London) **187**: 1130, 1960.

203. Siskind, G. W., Paterson, P. Y., and Thomas, L. Induction of unresponsiveness and immunity in newborn and adult mice with pneumococcal polysaccharide. *J. Immunol.* **90**:929-934, 1963.

204. Michie, D., and Howard, J. G. Transplantation tolerance and immunological immaturity. *Ann. New York Acad. Sc.* **99**: 670-679, 1962.

205. Uphoff, D. E. Drug-induced immunological "tolerance" for homotransplantation. *Transplantation Bull.* **28**:12-16, 1961.

206. Uphoff, D. E., and Pitkin, L. Drug-induced immunologic "tolerance" for homotransplantation of skin. *Blood* **20**:113, 1962.

207. McLaren, A. Induction of tolerance to skin homografts in adult mice treated with 6-mercaptopurine. *Transplantation Bull.* **28**:99-104, 1961.

208. Davis, W. E., Jr., and Cole, L. J. Homograft tolerance in mice: use of Urethane and sublethal irradiation. *Science* **140**:483, 1963.

209. Michie, D., and Woodruff, M. F. A. Induction of specific immunological tolerance of homografts in adult mice by sublethal irradiation and injection of donor-type spleen cells in high dosage. *Proc. Roy. Soc., London, s. B.* **156**:280-288, 1962.

210. Mannick, J. A., Lee, H. M., and Egdahl, R. H. Effect of 6-mercaptopurine on immune responsiveness of dog. *Surg., Gynec. & Obst.* **114**:449-457, 1962.

211. Linder, O. E. A. Unresponsiveness of adult female mice to male skin isografts after pretreatment with cells and homogenates from males. *Transplantation Bull.* **28**:36-39, 1961.

212. Billingham, R. E., and Silvers, W. K. Studies on tolerance of Y chromosome antigen in mice. *J. Immunol.* **85**:14-26, 1960.

213. Martinez, C., Smith, J. M., Blaese, M., and Good, R. A. Production of immunological tolerance in mice after repeated injections of disrupted spleen cells. *J. Exper. Med.* **118**:743-758, 1963.

214. Simonsen, M. Graft versus host reaction: their natural history, and applicability as tools of research. *Progr. in Allergy* **6**:349-467, 1962.

215. *Idem.* Impact on developing embryo and newborn animal of adult homologous cells. *Acta path. et microbiol. Scandinav.* **40**: 480-500, 1957.
216. Billingham, R. E., and Brent, L. Simple method for inducing tolerance of skin homografts in mice. *Transplantation Bull.* **4**:67-71, 1957.
217. *Idem.* Quantitative studies on tissue transplantation immunity. IV. Induction of tolerance in newborn mice and studies on phenomenon of runt disease. *Philos. Tr. Roy. Soc., London* **242**: 439-477, 1959.
218. Gowans, J. L., Gesner, B. M., and McGregor, D. D. Immunological activity of lymphocytes. In Ciba Foundation Study Group No. 10. *Biological Activity of the Leucocyte.* Edited by G. E. W. Wolstenholme and M. O'Connor. 128 pp. Boston: Little, Brown, 1961. Pp. 32-40.
219. Russell, P. S. Weight-gain assay for runt disease in mice. *Ann. New York Acad. Sc.* **87**:445-451, 1960.
220. Billingham, R. E., Brown, J. B., Defendi, V., Silvers, W. K., and Steinmuller, D. Quantitative studies on induction of tolerance of homologous tissues and on runt disease in rat. *Ann. New York Acad. Sc.* **87**:457-471, 1960.
221. Simonsen, M., Engelbreth-Holm, J., Jensen, E., and Poulsen, H. Study of graft-versus-host reaction in transplantation to embryos, F_1 hybrids, and irradiated animals. *Ann. New York Acad. Sc.* **73**:834-841. 1958.
222. Simonsen, M., and Jensen, E. Graft versus host assay in transplantation chimeras. In Symposium on Biological Problems of Grafting. *Biological Problems of Grafting: A symposium sponsored by the Comm. administrative de Liège and the Council for International Organizations of Medical Sciences.* Edited by F. Albert and P. B. Medawar. 453 pp. Oxford: Blackwell, 1959. Pp. 214-236.
223. Siskind, G., Leonard, L., and Thomas, L. Runting syndrome. *Ann. New York Acad. Sc.* **87**:452-456, 1960.
224. Dempster, W. J. Kidney homotransplantation. *Brit. J. Surg.* **40**:447-465, 1953.
225. Simonsen, M. Biological incompatibility in kidney transplantation in dogs. II. Serological investigations. *Acta path. et microbiol. Scandinav.* **32**:36-84, 1953.
226. Fowler, R., Jr., and West, C. D. Evidence against "graft-versus-host" hypothesis in renal transplantation. *Transplantation Bull.* **26**:133-141, 1960.
227. Hume, D. M., et al. Homotransplantation of kidneys and of fetal liver and spleen after total body irradiation. *Ann. Surg.* **152**:354-373, 1960.
228. Porter, K. A., and Calne, R. Y. Origin of infiltrating cells in skin and kidney homografts. *Plast. & Reconstruct. Surg.* **26**: 458-464, 1960.
229. Kaliss, N. Elements of immunologic enhancement: consideration of mechanisms. *Ann. New York Acad. Sc.* **101**:64-79, 1962.
230. *Idem.* Immunological enhancement of tumor homografts in mice: review. *Cancer Research* **18**:992-1003, 1958.
231. Kandutsch, A. A., and Reinert-Wenck, U. Studies on substance that promotes tumor homograft survival ("enhancing substance"). *J. Exper. Med.* **105**:125-139, 1957.
232. Kaliss, N. Regression or survival of tumor homografts in mice pretreated with injections of lyophilized tissues. *Cancer Research* **12**:379-382, 1952.
233. Hašková, V., and Svoboda, J. Relationship between transplantation immunity and immunological enhancement. In Symposium on Mechanisms of Immunological Tolerance, Liblice, 1961.

Mechanisms of Immunological Tolerance: Proceedings of a symposium held at Liblice near Prague, November 8-10, 1961. Edited by M. Hašek et al. 544 pp. New York: Academic Press, 1962. (Symposia CSAV, sv5.) Pp. 431-434.

234. Kaliss, N. Induction of homograft reaction in presence of immunological enhancement of tumor homografts. In Symposium on Mechanisms of Immunological Tolerance, Liblice, 1961. *Mechanisms of Immunological Tolerance: Proceedings of a symposium held at Liblice near Prague, November 8-10, 1961.* Edited by M. Hašek, et al. 544 pp. New York: Academic Press, 1962. (Symposia CSAV, sv5.) Pp. 413-429.

235. Kaliss, N., and Bryant, B. F. Factors determining homograft destruction and immunological enhancement in mice receiving successive tumor inocula. *J. Nat. Cancer Inst.* **20**:691-704, 1958.

236. Feldman, M., and Globerson, A. Studies on mechanism of immunological enhancement of tumor grafts. *J. Nat. Cancer Inst.* **25**:631-648, 1960.

237. Gorer, P. A. Antigenic structure of tumors. *Advances in Immunol.* **1**:345-393, 1961.

238. *Idem.* Interactions between sessile and humoral antibodies in homograft reactions. In *Ciba Foundation Symposium on Cellular Aspects of Immunity.* Edited by G. E. W. Wolstenholme and M. O'Connor. 494 pp. Boston: Little, Brown, 1960. Pp. 330-343.

239. Batchelor, J. R. Memorial lecture to Dr. Peter Alfred Gorer, F.R.S. In Symposium on Tissue Transplantation. *Proceedings of the International Symposium on Tissue Transplantation: Held in Vina del mar. Valparaiso in Chile, August 30-September 2, 1961.* Edited by A. P. Cristoffanini and G. Hoecker. 269 pp. Santiago, de Chile: Universidad de Chile, 1962. Pp. 121-137.

240. Boyse, E. A., Old, L. J., and Stockert, E. Some further data on cytotoxic isoantibodies in mouse. *Ann. New York Acad. Sc.* **99**:574-587, 1962.

241. Billingham, R. E., Brent, L., and Medawar, P. B. 'Enhancement' in normal homografts, with note on its possible mechanism. *Transplantation Bull.* **3**:84-88, 1956.

242. Snell, G. D. Homograft reaction. *Ann. Rev. Microbiol.* **11**:439-458, 1957.

243. Kaliss, N. Acceptance of tumor homografts by mice injected with antiserum. II. Effect of time of injection. *Proc. Soc. Exper. Biol. & Med.* **91**:432-437, 1956.

244. Gorer, P. A. Some reactions of H-2 antibodies *in vitro* and *in vivo*. *Ann. New York Acad. Sc.* **73**:707-721, 1958.

245. Batchelor, J. R., Boyse, E. A., and Gorer, P. A. Synergic action between isoantibody and immune cells in graft rejection. *Transplantation Bull.* **26**:449-453, 1960.

246. Amos, D. B. Possible relationships between cytotoxic effects of isoantibody and host cell function. *Ann. New York Acad. Sc.* **87**:273-290, 1960.

247. Snell, G. D., Winn, H. J., Stimpfling, J. H., and Parker, S. J. Depression by antibody of immune response to homografts and its role in immunological enhancement. *J. Exper. Med.* **112**:293-314, 1960.

248. Halasz, N. A., and Orloff, M. J. Enhancement of kidney homografts. *S. Forum* **14**:206-208, 1963.

249. Halasz, N. A. Enhancement of skin homografts in dogs. *J. S. Research* **3**:503-505, 1963.

250. Dixon, F. J., Talmage, W., and Maurer, P. H. Radiosensitive and radioresistant phases in antibody response. *J. Immunol.* **68**:693-700, 1952.

251. Taliaferro, W. H. Modification of immune response by radiation and cortisone. *Ann. New York Acad. Sc.* **69**:745-764, 1957.

252. Makinodan, T., and Gengozian, N. Effect of radiation on antibody formation. In *Radiation Protection and Recovery*. Edited by A. Hollaender. 392 pp. New York: Pergamon, 1960. Pp. 316-351.

253. *Idem.* Primary antibody response to distantly related heterologous antigen during maximum depression period after varying doses of X radiation. *J. Immunol.* **81**:150-154, 1958.

254. Dempster, W. J., Lennox, B., and Boag, J. W. Prolongation of survival of skin homotransplants in rabbit by irradiation of host. *Brit. J. Exper. Path.* **31**:670-679, 1950.

255. Kent, M. Experiments in homograft survival. In *Radiation Biology: Proceedings of the Second Australian Conference on Radiation Biology*. Edited by J. H. Martin. 364 pp. New York: Academic Press, 1959. Pp. 68-71.

256. McKhann, C. F. Effect of x-ray on antigenicity of donor cells in transplantation immunity. *J. Immunol.* **92**:811-815, 1964.

257. Monaco, A. P., and Mandel, M. A. Unpublished data.

258. Jacobson, L. O., Marks, E. K., Gaston, E. O., Robson, G. M., and Zirkle, R. E. Role of spleen in radiation injury. *Proc. Soc. Exper. Biol. & Med.* **70**:740-742, 1949.

259. Jacobson, L. O., Simmons, E. L., Bethard, W. F., Marks, E. K., and Robson, M. J. Influence of spleen on hematopoietic recovery after irradiation injury. *Proc. Soc. Exper. Biol. & Med.* **73**:455-459, 1950.

260. Jacobson, L. O., et al. Role of spleen in radiation injury and recovery. *J. Lab. & Clin. Med.* **35**:746-770, 1950.

261. Jacobson, L. O., Simmons, E. L., Marks, E. K., and Eldredge, J. H. Recovery from radiation injury. *Science* **113**:510, 1951.

262. Jacobson, L. O., et al. Further studies on recovery from radiation injury. *J. Lab. & Clin. Med.* **37**:683-697, 1951.

263. Jacobson, L. O. Evidence for humoral factor (or factors) concerned in recovery from radiation injury: review. *Cancer Research* **12**:315-325, 1952.

264. Lorenz, E., Congdon, C. C., and Uphoff, D. Modification of acute irradiation injury in mice and guinea-pigs by bone marrow injections. *Radiology* **58**:863-877, 1952.

265. Main, J. M., and Prehn, R. T. Successful skin homografts after administration of high dosage X radiation and homologous bone marrow. *J. Nat. Cancer Inst.* **15**:1023-1029, 1955.

266. Lindsley, D. L., Odell, T. T., Jr., and Tausche, F. G. Implantation of functional erythropoietic elements following total-body irradiation. *Proc. Soc. Exper. Biol. & Med.* **90**:512-515, 1955.

267. *Idem.* Implantation of functional erythropoietic elements following total body irradiation. *Transplantation Bull.* **3**:68, 1956.

268. Ford, C. E., Hamerton, J. L., Barnes, D. W. H., and Loutit, J. F. Cytological identification of radiation-chimaeras. *Nature* (London) **177**:452-454, 1956.

269. Vos, O., Davids, J. A. G., Weyzen, W. W. H., and van Bekkum, D. W. Evidence for cellular hypothesis in radiation protection by bone marrow cells. *Acta physiol. et pharmacol. neerl.* **4**:482-486, 1956.

270. Makinodan, T. Circulating rat cells in lethally irradiated mice protected with rat bone marrow. *Proc. Soc. Exper. Biol. & Med.* **92**:174-179, 1956.

271. Koller, P. C., Davies, A. J. S., and Doak, S. M. A. Radiation chimeras. In *Advances in Cancer Research* **6**:181-289, 1961.

272. van Bekkum, D. W., and Vos, O. Immunological aspects of homo- and heterologous bone marrow transplantation in irradiated animals. *J. Cell. & Comp. Physiol.* **50**:139-156, 1957.

273. Hollingsworth, J. W. Compatibility factors influencing acceptance of rat bone marrow graft by irradiated mouse. *Yale J. Biol. & Med.* **31**:157-163, 1958.

274. Brown, M. B., et al. Some biological aspects of factor in bone marrow responsible for hematopoietic recovery following systemic irradiation. *J. Nat. Cancer Inst.* **15**:949-973, 1955.

275. van Bekkum, D. W., Vos, O., and Weyzen, W. W. H. Homo- et hétérogreffe de tissus hématopoiétiques chez la souris. *Rev. d'hémat.* **11**:477-485, 1956.

276. Gengozian, N., and Makinodan, T. Relation of primary antigen injection to time of irradiation on antibody production in mice. *J. Immunol.* **80**:189-197, 1958.

277. Carter, T. C., Lyon, M. F., and Phillips, R. J. S. Gene-tagged chromosome translocations in eleven stocks of mice. *J. Genetics* **53**:154-166, 1955.

278. Porter, K. A. Effect of homologous bone marrow injections in x-irradiated rabbits. *Brit. J. Exper. Path.* **38**:401-412, 1957.

279. *Idem.* Use of sex difference in morphology of polymorphonuclear leucocytes to indicate survival of marrow homotransplants. *Transplantation Bull.* **4**:129, 1957.

280. Davidson, W. M., Fowler, J. F., and Smith, D. R. Sexing neutrophil leucocytes in natural and artificial blood chimaeras. *Brit. J. Haemat.* **4**:231-238, 1958.

281. Owen, R. E. Erythrocyte repopulation following transplantation of homologous erythropoietic tissues into irradiated mice. In *Symposium on Biological Problems of Grafting. Biological Problems of Grafting: A symposium sponsored by the Comm. administrative de Liège and the Council for International Organizations of Medical Sciences.* Edited by F. Albert and P. B. Medawar. 453 pp. Oxford: Blackwell, 1959. Pp. 260-273.

282. Mitchison, N. A. Colonisation of irradiated tissue by transplanted spleen cells. *Brit. J. Exper. Path.* **37**:239-247, 1956.

283. Makinodan, T. Fate of injected rat bone marrow cells in irradiated mice. *J. Cell. & Comp. Physiol.* **50**:157-171, 1957.

284. Popp, R. A., and Smith, L. H. Electrophoresis of proteins of irradiated mouse chimeras. *J. Nat. Cancer Inst.* **23**:395-410, 1959.

285. Nowell, P. C., Cole, L. J., Roan, P. L., and Habermeyer, J. G. Distribution and *in situ* growth pattern of injected rat marrow in x-irradiated mice. *J. Nat. Cancer Inst.* **18**:127-143, 1957.

286. Congdon, C. C. Recovery from radiation injury, with special consideration of use of bone marrow transplantation. *Progr. in Hemat.* **2**:21-46, 1959.

287. Gengozian, N., and Makinodan, T. Mortality of mice as affected by variation of x-ray dose and number of nucleated rat bone marrow cells injected. *Cancer Research* **17**:970-975, 1957.

288. Ford, C. E. Studies of radiation chimaeras by use of chromosome markers. In *Advances in Radiobiology: Proceedings of the Fifth International Conference on Radiobiology.* Edited by G. de Hevesy, A. Forssberg and J. D. Abbott. 503 pp. London: Oliver, 1957. Pp. 197-203.

289. Welling, W., Vos, O., Weyzen, W. W. H., and van Bekkum D. W. Identification and follow-up of homologous and heterologous bone-marrow transplants in radiation-chimeras. *Internat. J. Radiat. Biol.* **1**:143-152, 1959.

290. Barnes, D. W. H., Ford, C. E., Gray, S. M., and Loutit, J. F. Grafting rat skin to mouse/rat chimeras. In *Symposium on Biological Problems of Grafting. Biological Problems of Grafting: A symposium sponsored by the Comm. administrative de Liège and the Council for International Organizations of Medical Sciences.* Edited by F. Albert and P. B. Medawar. 453 pp. Oxford: Blackwell, 1959. Pp. 274-291.

177

291. Trentin, J. J. Induced tolerance and "homologous disease" in x-irradiated mice protected with homologous bone marrow. *Proc. Soc. Exper. Biol. & Med.* **96**:139-144, 1957.

292. Congdon, C. C., and Urso, I. S. Homologous bone marrow in treatment of radiation injury in mice. *Am. J. Path.* **33**:749-767, 1957.

293. Smith, L. H., and Congdon, C. C. Experimental treatment of acute whole-body radiation injury in mammals. In *Radiation Protection and Recovery*. Edited by A. Hollaender. 392 pp. New York: Pergamon, 1960. Pp. 242-302.

294. Kaplan, H. S., and Rosston, B. H. Amelioration by adrenalectomy of homologous wasting disease induced in irradiated hybrid mice by injection of parental lymphoid cells. *Transplantation Bull.* **6**:107-109, 1959.

295. Gengozian, N., and Makinodan, T. Antibody response of lethally x-irradiated mice treated with rat bone marrow. *J. Immunol.* **77**:430-436, 1956.

296. Barnes, D. W. H., Ford, C. E., Ilbery, P. L. T., and Loutit, J. F. Tolerance in radiation chimaera. *Transplantation Bull.* **5**:101-106, 1958.

297. Koller, P. C., and Doak, S. M. A. Effect of radiation on immune response in mice and its modification by tissue transplantation. *Internat. J. Radiat. Biol.* Pp. 327-342, 1960.

298. Cole, L. J., and Garver, R. M. Studies on mechanism of secondary disease: parental-F₁ hybrid radiation chimera. *Radiat. Research* **12**:398-408, 1960.

299. Congdon, C. C., and Urso, I. Isologous versus homologous bone marrow in treatment of irradiated mice. *Radiat. Research* **5**:474, 1956.

300. Uphoff, D. E. Preclusion of secondary phase of irradiation syndrome by inoculation of fetal hematopoietic tissue following lethal total-body x-irradiation. *J. Nat. Cancer Inst.* **20**:625-632, 1958.

301. Urso, I. Long-term survival of lethally irradiated mice treated with hematopoietic tissues from fetal and newborn homologous and heterologous donors. *Radiat. Research* **9**:197, 1958.

302. Urso, I. S., Congdon, C. C., and Owen, R. D. Effects of foreign fetal and newborn blood-forming tissues on survival of lethally irradiated mice. *Proc. Soc. Exper. Biol. & Med.* **100**:395-399, 1959.

303. Porter, K. A. Marrow transplantation after radiation: experimental approach to immunological complications. *Clin. Radiat.* **11**:22-32, 1960.

304. Miller, J. F. A. P. Immunological function of thymus. *Lancet* **2**:748, 1961.

305. Martinez, C., Kersey, J., Papermaster, B. W., and Good, R. A. Skin homograft survival in thymectomized mice. *Proc. Soc. Exper. Biol. & Med.* **109**:193-196, 1962.

306. Miller, J. F. A. P., Marshall, A. H. E., and White, R. G. Immunological significance of thymus. *Advances in Immunol.* **2**:111-162, 1962.

307. Arnason, B. G., and Janković, B. D. Suppression of "delayed" hypersensitivity reactions in rats thymectomized at birth. *Federation Proc.* **21**:274, 1962.

308. Arnason, B. G., Janković, B. D., and Waksman, B. H. Effect of thymectomy on 'delayed' hypersensitive reactions. *Nature (London)* **194**:99, 1962.

309. Miller, J. F. A. P. Etiology and pathogenesis of mouse leukemia. *Advances in Cancer Research* **6**:291-368, 1961.

310. Idem. Rôle of thymus in transplantation tolerance and immunity. In *Ciba Foundation Symposium on Transplantation*. Edited by G. E. W. Wolstenholme and M. P. Cameron. 426 pp. Boston: Little, Brown, 1962. Pp. 384-397.

311. *Idem.* Effect of neonatal thymectomy on immunological responsiveness of mouse. *Proc. Roy. Soc., London, s. B.* **156**: 415-428, 1962.
312. Waksman, B. H., Arnason, B. G., and Jankovic, B. D. Changes in lymphoid organs of rats thymectomized at birth. *Federation Proc.* **21**:274, 1962.
313. Parrot, D. M. V. Strain variation in mortality and runt disease in mice thymectomized at birth. *Transplantation Bull.* **29**:102-104, 1962.
314. Waksman, B. H., Arnason, B. G., and Janković, B. D. Role of thymus in immune reactions in rats. III. Changes in lymphoid organs of thymectomized rats. *J. Exper. Med.* **116**:187-206, 1962.
315. Harris, T. N., Rhoads, J. E., and Stokes, J., Jr. Study of role of thymus and spleen in formation of antibodies in rabbit. *J. Immunol.* **58**:27-32, 1948.
316. MacLean, L. D., Zak, S. J., Varco, R. L., and Good, R. A. Role of thymus in antibody production: experimental study of immune response in thymectomized rabbits. *Transplantation Bull.* **4**:21, 1957.
317. Fichtelius, K., Laurell, G., and Philipsson, L. Influence of thymectomy on antibody formation. *Acta path. et microbiol. Scandinav.* **51**:81-86, 1961.
318. Archer, O., and Pierce, J. C. Role of thymus in development of immune response. *Federation Proc.* **20**:26, 1961.
319. Miller, J. F. A. P. Analysis of thymus influence in leukaemogenesis. *Nature* (London) **191**:248, 1961.
320. *Idem.* Role of thymus in transplantation immunity. *Ann. New York Acad. Sc.* **99**:340-354, 1962.
321. Sherman, J. D., and Dameshek, W. "Wasting disease" following thymectomy in hamster. *Nature* (London) **197**:469-471, 1963.
322. Dalmasso, A. P., Martinez, C., and Good, R. A. Failure of spleen cells from thymectomized mice to induce graft vs. host reactions. *Proc. Soc. Exper. Biol. & Med.* **110**:205-208, 1962.
323. Metcalf, D. Effect of thymectomy on lymphoid tissues of mouse. *Brit. J. Haemat.* **6**:324-333, 1960.
324. Miller, J. F. A. P. Immunological significance of thymus of adult mouse. *Nature* (London) **195**:1318, 1962.
325. Auerbach, R. Thymus: its role in lymphoid recovery after irradiation. *Science* **139**:1061, 1963.
326. Miller, J. F. A. P., Doak, S. M. A., and Cross, A. M. Role of thymus in recovery of immune mechanism in irradiated adult mouse. *Proc. Soc. Exper. Biol. & Med.* **112**:785-792, 1963.
327. Cross, A. M., Leuchars, E., and Miller, J. F. A. P. Studies on recovery of immune response in irradiated mice thymectomized in adult life. *J. Exper. Med.* **119**:837-850, 1964.
328. Claman, H. N., and Talmage, D. W. Thymectomy: prolongation of immunological tolerance in adult mouse. *Science* **141**:1193, 1963.
329. Nossal, G. V. J. Studies on rate of seeding of lymphocytes from the intact guinea-pig thymus. *Ann. New York Acad. Sc.* **120**:171-181, 1964.
330. Miller, J. F. A. P. In *The Thymus in Immunobiology.* Edited by R. A. Good and A. E. Gabrielson. New York: Harper, 1964.
331. *Idem.* Immunity and thymus. *Lancet* **1**:43-45, 1963.
332. Law, L. W., and Miller, J. H. Influence of thymectomy on incidence of carcinogen-induced leukemia in strain DBA mice. *J. Nat. Cancer Inst.* **11**:425-438, 1950.
333. Loutit, J. F. In *Ciba Foundation Symposium on Transplantation.* Edited by G. E. W. Wolstenholme and M. P. Cameron. 426 pp. Boston: Little, Brown, 1962. P. 399.
334. Auerbach, R. Experimental analysis of origin of cell types in development of mouse thymus. *Developmental Biol.* **3**:336-354, 1961.

335. Auerbach, R. *J. Nat. Cancer Inst.* Monogr. **10**:1962.

336. Levey, R. H., Trainin, N., and Law, L. W. Evidence for function of thymic tissue in diffusion chambers implanted in neonatally thymectomized mice: preliminary report. *J. Nat. Cancer Inst.* **31**:199-218, 1963.

337. Levey, R. H., Trainin, N., Law, L. W., Black, P. H., and Rowe, W. P. Lymphocytic choriomeningitis infection in neonatally thymectomized mice bearing diffusion chambers containing thymus. *Science* **142**:483-485, 1963.

338. Osoba, D., and Miller, J. F. A. P. Lymphoid tissues and immune responses of neonatally thymectomized mice bearing thymus tissue in millipore diffusion chambers. *J. Exper. Med.* **119**:177-194, 1964.

339. Law, L. W., Trainin, N., Levey, R. H., and Barth, W. F. Humoral thymic factor in mice: further evidence. *Science* **143**: 1049-1051, 1964.

340. Miller, J. F. A. P., Leuchars, E., Cross, A. M., Davies, A. J. S., and Dukor, P. Immunological role of the thymus in radiation chimeras. *Ann. New York Acad. Sc.* **120**:205-217, 1964.

341. Nelson, C. T., Fox, C. L., and Freeman, E. B. Inhibitory effect of cortisone on anaphylaxis in mouse. *Proc. Soc. Exper. Biol. & Med.* **75**:181-183, 1950.

342. Dews, P. B., and Code, C. F. Anaphylactic reactions and concentrations of antibody in rats and rabbits: effect of adrenalectomy and of administration of cortisone. *J. Immunol.* **70**:199-206, 1953.

343. Solotorovsky, M., and Winsten, S. Inhibition of fatal anaphylactic shock in mouse with cortisone. *J. Immunol.* **72**:177, 1954.

344. Moyer, A. W., Jervis, G. A., Black, J., Koprowski, H., and Cox, H. R. Action of adrenocorticotropic hormone (ACTH) in experimental allergic encephalomyelitis of guinea pig. *Proc. Soc. Exper. Biol. & Med.* **75**:387-390, 1950.

345. Long, J. B., and Favour, C. B. Ability of ACTH and cortisone to alter delayed type bacterial hypersensitivity. *Bull. Johns Hopkins Hosp.* **87**:186-202, 1950.

346. Germuth, F. G., Jr., and Ottinger, B. Effect of 17-hydroxy-11-dehydrocorticosterone (Compound E) and of ACTH on Arthus reaction and antibody formation in rabbit. *Proc. Soc. Exper. Biol. & Med.* **74**:815-823, 1950.

347. Berglund, K. Studies on factors which condition effect of cortisone on antibody production. I. Significance of time of hormone administration in primary hemolysin response. *Acta path. et microbiol. Scandinav.* **38**:311-328, 1956.

348. Toolan, H. W. Conditioning of host. *J. Nat. Cancer Inst.* **14**:745-765, 1953.

349. Woolley, G. W., and Harris, J. J. Steroids effects on heterologously transplanted human tumors. In Conference on the Biologically Activities of Steroids in Relation to Cancer, Vergennes, Vermont, 1959. *Biological Activities of Steroids in Relation to Cancer: Proceedings of a conference sponsored by the Cancer Chemotherapy National Service Center, National Cancer Institute, National Institutes of Health, United States Department of Health, Education, and Welfare.* Edited by G. Pincus and E. P. Vollmer. 530 pp. New York: Academic Press, 1960. Pp. 307-330.

350. Billingham, R. E., Krohn, P. L., and Medawar, P. B. Effect of cortisone on survival of skin homograft in rabbits. *Brit. M. J.* **1**:1157-1163, 1951.

351. Sparrow, E. M. Behaviour of skin autografts and skin homografts in guinea-pig, with special reference to effect of cortisone acetate and ascorbic acid on homograft reaction. *J. Endocrinol.* **9**:101-113, 1953.

352. Medawar, P. B., and Sparrow, E. M. Effects of adrenocortical hormones, adrenocorticotrophic hormone and pregnancy on skin transplantation immunity in mice. *J. Endocrinol.* **14**:240-256, 1956.
353. Cannon, J. A., and Longmire, W. P., Jr. Studies of successful skin homografts in chicken: description of method of grafting and its application as technique of investigation. *Ann. Surg.* **135**:60-68, 1952.
354. Krohn, P. L. Effect of ACTH and cortisone on survival of skin homografts and on adrenal glands in monkeys *(Macaca mulatta)*. *J. Endocrinol.* **12**:220-226, 1955.
355. Darcy, D. Host response to frozen-thawed homografts. *Transplantation Bull.* **2**:47-49, 1955.
356. Zukoski, C. F., and Callaway, J. M. Effect of B.W. 57-322, 6-methylmercaptopurine, urethane plus 6-azauracil and prednisolone on renal homograft survival. *Federation Proc.* **21**:39, 1962.
357. Zukoski, C. F., Callaway, J. M., and Rhea, W. G., Jr. Tolerance to canine renal homograft induced by prednisolone. *S. Forum* **14**:208-210, 1963.
358. Calne, R. Y., Alexandre, G. P. J., and Murray, J. E. Study of effects of drugs in prolonging survival of homologous renal transplants in dogs. *Ann. New York Acad. Sc.* **99**:743-761, 1962.
359. Murray, J. E. Human kidney transplant conference (Sept. 26-27, 1963). *Transplantation* **2**:147-155, 1964.
360. Scothorne, R. J. Effect of cortisone on cellular changes in regional lymph node draining skin homograft. *Transplantation Bull.* **3**:13, 1956.
361. Menkin, V. *Biochemical Mechanisms in Inflammation.* Second edition. 440 pp. Springfield, Illinois: Thomas, 1956. P. 364.
362. Schwartz, R., Stack, J., and Dameshek, W. Effect of 6-mercaptopurine on antibody production. *Proc. Soc. Exper. Biol. & Med.* **99**:164-167, 1958.
363. Schwartz, R. S., and André, J. Clearance of proteins from blood of normal and 6-mercaptopurine treated rabbits. *Proc. Soc. Exper. Biol. & Med.* **104**:228-230, 1960.
364. Schwartz, R., Eisner, A., and Dameshek, W. Effect of 6-mercaptopurine on primary and secondary immune responses. *J. Clin. Investigation* **38**:1394-1403, 1959.
365. Schwartz, R., and Dameshek, W. Drug-induced immunological tolerance. *Nature* (London) **183**:1682, 1959.
366. Feldman, M., Gloverson, A., and Nachtigal, D. Reactivation of immune response in immunologically suppressed animals. *Transplantation Bull.* **30**:105, 1962.
367. Genghof, D., and Battisto, J. R. Antibody production in guinea pigs receiving 6-mercaptopurine. *Proc. Soc. Exper. Biol. & Med.* **107**:933-936, 1961.
368. Smith, R. T. Immunological tolerance of nonliving antigens. *Advances in Immunol.* **1**:67-129, 1961.
369. Condie, R. M., and Forsen, N. R. Delayed treatment of immune processes with 6-mercaptopurine. *Blood* **20**:113, 1962.
370. LaPlante, E. S., Condie, R. M., and Good, R. A. Prevention of secondary immune response with 6-mercaptopurine. *J. Lab. & Clin. Med.* **59**:542-549, 1962.
371. Hoyer, J. R., Hoyer, L. W., Good, R. A., and Condie, R. M. Effect of 6-mercaptopurine on delayed hypersensitivity in guinea pigs. *J. Exper. Med.* **116**:679-685, 1962.
372. Thompson, J. D., and Austin, R. W. Effects of 6-mercaptopurine on susceptibility of guinea pigs to experimental allergic encephalomyelitis. *Proc. Soc. Exper. Biol. & Med.* **111**:121-123, 1962.
373. Janssen, R. J., Marshall, R. G., Gerone, P. J., Cheville, N. F., and Convey, J. H. Effects of 6-mercaptopurine on immunological responses of various laboratory animals to variola and vaccinia viruses. *Bact. Proc.* **14**:120, 1961.

374. Sterzl, J., and Holub, M. Influence of 6-mercaptopurine on antibody formation. *Folia biol.* **4**:59-61, 1958.
375. Schwartz, R., and Dameshek, W. Effects of 6-mercaptopurine on homograft reactions. *J. Clin. Investigation* **39**:952-958, 1960.
376. Thomas, A. N., Morton, D. L., Crane, J. T., and Gardner, R. E. Effect of 6-mercaptopurine on homograft reaction in rats. *Proc. Soc. Exper. Biol. & Med.* **107**:70, 1961.
377. André, J. A., Schwartz, R. S., Mitus, W. J., and Dameshek, W. Morphologic responses of lymphoid system to homografts. I. First and second set responses in normal rabbits. *Blood* **19**:313-333, 1962.
378. *Idem.* Morphologic responses of lymphoid system to homografts. II. Effects of antimetabolites. *Blood* **19**:334-348, 1962.
379. Calne, R. Y. Rejection of renal homografts: inhibition in dogs by 6-mercaptopurine. *Lancet* **1**:417, 1960.
380. *Idem.* Observations on renal homotransplantation. *Brit. J. Surg.* **48**:384-391, 1961.
381. Zukoski, C. F., Lee, H. M., and Hume, D. M. Prolongation of functional survival of canine renal homografts by 6-mercaptopurine. *S. Forum* **11**:470-472, 1960.
382. Zukoski, C. F., Lee, H. M., and Hume, D. M. Effect of antimetabolites on prolonging functional survival of canine renal homografts: 6-mercaptopurine, 8-azaguanine. *Federation Proc.* **20**:34, 1961.
383. *Idem.* Effect of 6-mercaptopurine on renal homograft survival in dog. *Surg., Gynec. & Obst.* **112**:707-714, 1961.
384. Pierce, J. C., Varco, R. L., and Good, R. A. Prolonged survival of renal homograft in dog treated with 6-mercaptopurine. *Surgery* **50**:186-195, 1961.
385. Zukoski, C. F., Lee, H. M., and Hume, D. M. Effect of antimetabolites on prolonging functional survival of canine renal homografts. *J. S. Research* **2**:44-48, 1962.
386. Calne, R. Y. Inhibition of rejection of renal homografts in dogs by purine analogues. *Transplantation Bull.* **28**:65-81, 1961.
387. Alexandre, G. P. J., and Murray, J. E. Further studies of renal homotransplantation in dogs treated by combined imuran therapy. *S. Forum* **13**:64-66, 1962.
388. Berenbaum, M. C. Effect of cytotoxic agents on production of antibody to T.A.B. vaccine in mouse. *Biochem. Pharmacol.* **11**:29-44, 1962.
389. Uphoff, D. E. Alteration of homograft reaction by A-methopterin in lethally irradiated mice treated with homologous marrow. *Proc. Soc. Exper. Biol. & Med.* **99**:651-653, 1958.
390. Friedman, R. M., Buckler, C. E., and Baron, S. Effect of aminomethylpteroylglutamic acid on development of skin hypersensitivity and on antibody formation in guinea pigs. *J. Exper. Med.* **114**:173-183, 1961.
391. Philips, F. S., Hopkins, F. H., and Freeman, M. L. H. Effect of tris (betachloroethyl) amine on antibody-production in goats. *J. Immunol.* **55**:289-296, 1947.
392. Spurr, C. L. Influence of nitrogen mustards on antibody response. *Proc. Soc. Exper. Biol. & Med.* **64**:259-261, 1947.
393. Taliaferro, W. H., and Taliaferro, L. G. Reduction in immunity in chicken malaria following treatment with nitrogen mustard. *J. Infect. Dis.* **82**:5-30, 1948.
394. Schwab, L., et al. Experimental hypersensitivity in rabbit: effect of inhibition of antibody formation by x-radiation and nitrogen mustard on histologic and serologic sequences, and on behavior of serum complement, following single large injections of foreign proteins. *J. Exper. Med.* **91**:505-526, 1950.
395. Berenbaum, M. C. Action of antimitotic substances on immune response. *Path. et biol.* **9**:963-966, 1961.

396. Brown, I. N., and Berenbaum, M. C. Inhibition of immune processes by "melphalan." *Nature* (London) **201**:1340, 1964.

397. Absolon, K. B., and Lenhardt, H. F. Effect of enzymatic agents, nitrogen mustard and Phenergan on autologous and homologous split thickness grafts in humans. *Plast. & Reconstruct. Surg.* **25**: 411-413, 1960.

398. McQuarrie, D. G., Condie, R. M., Mecher, W. R., Roller, F., and Varco, R. L. Effects of methyl bis (2-chloroethyl) amine upon survival of skin homografts in rats and rabbits. *Proc. Soc. Exper. Biol. & Med.* **103**:278-282, 1960.

399. Jones, J. W., Oneal, R., Haines, R., and Rosin, B. S. Prolongation of rabbit skin homografts with cyclophosphamide. *Federation Proc.* **21**:40, 1962.

400. Sutton, W. R., Griffith, H. B., and Preston, F. W. Effect of cancer chemotherapeutic agents on survival of homografts of skin. *S. Forum* **12**:117, 1961.

401. Berenbaum, M. C., and Brown, I. N. Prolongation of homograft survival in mice with single doses of cyclophosphamide. *Nature* (London) **200**:84, 1963.

402. Baker, R., Gordon, R., Huffer, J., and Miller, G. H., Jr. Experimental renal transplantation. I. Effect of nitrogen mustard, cortisone, and splenectomy. *Arch. Surg.* **65**:702-705, 1952.

403. Hurwitz, J., and August, J. T. Role of DNA in RNA synthesis. In *Progress in Nucleic Acid Research*. Edited by J. N. Davidson and W. E. Cohn. Vol. 1. 424 pp. New York: Academic Press, 1963. Pp. 59-92.

404. Guidice, G., and Novelli, G. D. Effect of actinomycin D on synthesis of DNA polymerase in hepatectomized rats. *Biochem. & Biophys. Research Commun.* **12**:383-387, 1963.

405. Uhr, J. W. Actinomycin D: its effect on antibody formation in vitro. *Science* **142**:1476, 1963.

406. Ambrose, C. T., and Coons, A. H. Personal communication.

407. Smiley, J. D., Heard, J. G., and Ziff, M. Effect of actinomycin D on RNA synthesis and antibody formation in anamnestic response *in vitro*. *J. Exper. Med.* **119**:881-893, 1964.

408. Wust, C. J., Gall, C. L., and Novelli, G. D. Actinomycin D: effect on immune response. *Science* **143**:1041-1043, 1964.

409. Nathan, H. C., Bieber, S., Elion, G. B., and Hitchings, G. H. Detection of agents which interfere with immune response. *Proc. Soc. Exper. Biol. & Med.* **107**:796-799, 1961.

410. Calne, R. Y., and Murray, J. E. Inhibition of rejection of renal homografts in dogs by Burroughs Wellcome 57-322. *S. Forum* **12**:118-120, 1961.

411. Shatkin, A. J., Reich, E., Franklin, R. M., and Tatum, E. L. Effect of mitomycin C on mammalian cells in culture. *Biochem. et biophys. acta* **55**:277-289, 1962.

412. Bloom, B. R., Hamilton, L. D., and Chase, M. W. Effects of mitomycin C on cellular transfer of delayed-type hypersensitivity in guinea pig. *Nature* (London) **201**:689-691, 1964.

413. Hitchings, G. H., and Elion, G. B. Chemical suppression of immune response. *Pharmacol. Rev.* **15**:365-405, 1963.

414. Hodes. M. E., Rohn, R. J., and Bond, W. H. Vincaleukoblastine. I. Preliminary clinical studies. *Cancer Research* **20**:1041-1049, 1960.

415. Warwick, O. H., Alison, R. E., and Darte, J. M. M. Clinical experience with vinblastine sulfate. *Canad. M. A. J.* **85**:579-583, 1961.

416. Aisenberg, A. C. Suppression of immune response by 'Vincristine' and 'Vinblastine.' *Nature* (London) **200**:484, 1963.

417. Farhi, A., and Lamensans, A. Contribution à l'étude de l'action des antibiotiques sur l'immunité. I. Action du chloramphénicol sur la production d'anticorps vis-à-vis d'un antigène soluble. *Compt. rend. Acad. d. sc.* **241**:1894-1896, 1955.

418. Butler, W. T. Effect of various pharmacological agents on secondary antibody response to diphtheria toxoid in mice. *Federation Proc.* **20**:27, 1961.

419. Ambrose, C. T., and Coons, A. H. Studies on antibody production. VIII. Inhibitory effect of chloramphenicol on synthesis of antibody in tissue culture. *J. Exper. Med.* **117**:1075-1088, 1963.

420. Weisberger, A., Daniel, T., and Hoffman, A. Suppression of antibody synthesis and prolongation of homograft survival by chloramphenicol. *J. Exper. Med.* **120**:183-196, 1964.

421. Woodruff, M. F. A. Transplantation of homologous tissue and its surgical applications: Hunterian lecture. *Ann. Roy. Coll. Surgeons England* **11**:173-194, 1952.

422. *Idem.* "Critical period" of homografts. *Transplantation Bull.* **1**: 221, 1954.

423. Weber, R. A., Cannon, J. A., and Longmire, W. P. Observations on regrafting of successful homografts in chickens. *Ann. Surg.* **139**:473-477, 1954.

424. Woodruff, M. F. A., and Simpson, L. O. Induction of tolerance to skin homografts in rats by injection of cells from prospective donor soon after birth. *Brit. J. Exper. Path.* **36**:494-499, 1955.

425. Stone, H. B., Eyring, J. R., Jr., and Kennedy, W. J. Survival of heterologous mammalian implants. *Ann. Surg.* **151**:626-629, 1960.

426. Stone, H. B., and Kennedy, W. J. Survival of heterologous mammalian transplants: further report. *Ann. Surg.* **155**:623-628, 1962.

427. *Idem.* Survival of heterologous mammalian transplants. *Ann. Surg.* **159**:645-651, 1964.

428. Murray, J. E., et al. Kidney transplantation in modified recipients. *Ann. Surg.* **156**:337-355, 1962.

429. Murray, J. E., Sheil, A. G. R., Moseley, R., Knight, P., McGarie, J. D., and Dammin, G. J. Analysis of mechanism of immunosuppressive drugs in renal homotransplantation. *Ann. Surg.* **160**: 449-473, 1964.

430. Hauschka, T. S., Kvedar, B. J., Grinnell, S. T., and Amos, D. B. Immunoselection of polyploids from predominantly diploid cell populations. *Ann. New York Acad. Sc.* **63**:683-705, 1956.

431. Koprowski, H., Theis, G., and Love, R. Immunological tolerance in tumour studies: adaptation of ascites tumours to homologous or heterologous hosts. *Proc. Roy. Soc., London, s. B.* **146**:37-57, 1956.

432. Lederberg, J. Prospects for genetics of somatic and tumor cells. *Ann. New York Acad. Sc.* **63**:662-665, 1956.

433. Good, R. A., Kelly, W. D., Rötstein, J., and Varco, R. L. Immunological deficiency diseases agammaglobulinemia, hypogammaglobulinemia, Hodgkin's disease and sarcoidosis. *Progr. in Allergy* **6**:187-316, 1962.

434. Good, R. A., and Varco, R. L. Successful homograft of skin in child with agammaglobulinemia: studies on agammaglobulinemia. *J.A.M.A.* **157**:713-716, 1955.

435. Good, R. A., Varco, R. L., Aust, J. B., and Zak, S. J. Transplantation studies in patients with agammaglobulinemia. *Ann. New York Acad. Sc.* **64**:882-928, 1957.

436. McLean, L. D., Zak, S. J., Varco, R. L., and Good, R. A. Thymic tumor and acquired agammaglobulinema: clinical and experimental study of immune response. *Surgery* **40**:1010-1017, 1956.

437. Giedion, A., and Scheidegger, J. J. Cited by Good, Kelly, Rötstein and Varco.[433]

438. Schubert, W. K., Fowler, R., Jr., Martin, L. W., and West, C. D. Homograft rejection in children with congenital immu-

nological defects: agammaglobulinemia and Aldrich syndrome. *Transplantation Bull.* **26**:125-128, 1960.

439. Martin, C. M., Waite, J. B., and McCullough, N. B. Antibody protein synthesis by lymph nodes homotransplanted to hypogammaglobulinemic adult. *J. Clin. Investigation* **36**:405-421, 1957.

440. Aisenberg, A. C. Immunologic aspects of Hodgkin's disease. *Medicine* **43**:189-193, 1964.

441. Parker, F., Jr., Jackson, H., Jr., Fitz Hugh, G., and Spies, T. D. Studies of diseases of lymphoid and myeloid tissues. IV. Skin reactions to human and avian tuberculin. *J. Immunol.* **22**:277-282, 1932.

442. Steiner, P. E. Etiology of Hodgkin's disease. II. Skin reactions to avian and human tuberculin proteins in Hodgkin's disease. *Arch. Int. Med.* **54**:11-17, 1934.

443. Schier, W. W., Roth, A., Ostroff, G., and Schrift, M. H. Hodgkin's disease and immunity. *Am. J. Med.* **20**:94-99, 1956.

444. Lamb, D., Pilney, F., Kelly, W. D., and Good, R. A. Comparative study of incidence of anergy in patients with carcinoma, leukemia, Hodgkin's disease and other lymphomas. *J. Immunol.* **89**:555-558, 1962.

445. Sokal, J. E., and Primikirios, N. Delayed skin test response in Hodgkin's disease and lymphosarcoma: effect of disease activity. *Cancer* **14**:597-607, 1961.

446. Aisenberg, A. C. Studies on delayed hypersensitivity in Hodgkin's disease. *J. Clin. Investigation* **41**:1964-1970, 1962.

447. Green, I., Inkelas, M., and Allen, L. B. Hodgkin's disease: maternal-to-foetal lymphocyte chimaera? *Lancet* **1**:30-32, 1960.

448. Kelly, W. D., Lamb, D. L., Varco, R. L., and Good, R. A. Investigation of Hodgkin's disease with respect to problem of homotransplantation. *Ann. New York Acad. Sc.* **87**:187-202, 1960.

449. Miller, D. G., Lizardo, J. G., and Snyderman, R. K. Homologous and heterologous skin transplantation in patients with lymphomatous disease. *J. Nat. Cancer Inst.* **26**:569-583, 1961.

450. Beilby, J. O. W., Cade, I. S., Jelliffe, A. M., Parkin, D. M., and Stewart, J. W. Prolonged survival of bone-marrow graft resulting in blood-group chimaera. *Brit. M. J.* **1**:96-99, 1960.

451. Green, I., and Corso, P. F. Study of skin homografting in patients with lymphomas. *Blood* **14**:235-245, 1959.

452. Southam, C. M., and Pillemer, L. Serum properdin levels and cancer cell homografts in man. *Proc. Soc. Exper. Biol. & Med.* **96**:596-601, 1957.

453. Kelly, W. D., Good, R. A., and Varco, R. L. Anergy and skin homograft survival in Hodgkin's disease. *Surg., Gynec. & Obst.* **107**:565-570, 1958.

454. Aisenberg, A. C., and Leskowitz, S. Antibody formation in Hodgkin's disease. *New Eng. J. Med.* **268**:1269-1272, 1963.

455. Riker, W., and Clark, M. Sarcoidosis: clinicopathologic review of three hundred cases, including twenty-two autopsies. *Am. J. Clin. Path.* **19**:725-749, 1949.

456. Lemming, R. Attempt to analyze tuberculin anergy in Schaumann's disease (Boeck's "sarcoid") and uveoparotid fever by means of BCG vaccination. *Acta med. Scandinav.* **103**:400-429, 1940.

457. Urbach, F., Sones, M., and Israel, H. L. Passive transfer of tuberculin sensitivity to patients with sarcoidosis. *New Eng. J. Med.* **247**:794-797, 1952.

458. Carnes, W. H., and Raffel, S. Comparison of sarcoidosis and tuberculosis with respect to complement fixation with antigens derived from tubercle bacillus. *Bull. Johns Hopkins Hosp.* **85**:204-220, 1949.

459. Sones, M., and Israel, H. L. Altered immunologic reactions in sarcoidosis. *Ann. Int. Med.* **40**:260-268, 1954.

460. Russell, P. S. Unpublished data.
461. Boder, E., and Sedgwick, R. P. Ataxia-telangiectasia: familial syndrome of progressive cerebellar ataxia, oculocutaneous telangiectasia and frequent pulmonary infection. *Pediatrics* **21**:526-553, 1958.
462. Peterson, R. D. A., Kelly, W. D., and Good, R. A. Ataxia-telangiectasia: its association with defective thymus, immunological-deficiency disease, and malignancy. *Lancet* **1**:1189-1193, 1964.
463. Fireman, P., Boesman, M., and Gitlin, D. Ataxia telangiectasia: dysgammaglobulinaemia with deficient γ_1 A (β_2A)-globulin. *Lancet* **1**:1193-1195, 1964.
464. Young, R. R., Austen, K. F., and Moser, H. W. Abnormalities of serum gamma 1A globulin and ataxia telangiectasia. *Medicine* **43**:423-433, 1964.
465. Billingham, R. E., and Silvers, W. K. Inbred animals and tissue transplantation immunity. *Transplantation Bull.* **6**:399-406, 1959.
466. Billingham, R. E., Hodge, B. A., and Silvers, W. K. Estimate of number of histocompatibility loci in rat. *Proc. Nat. Acad. Sc.* **48**:138-147, 1962.
467. Barnes, A. D., and Krohn, P. L. Estimation of number of histocompatibility genes controlling successful transplantation of normal skin in mice. *Proc. Roy. Soc., London, s. B.* **146**:505-526, 1957.
468. Snell, G. D., and Stevens, L. C. Histocompatibility genes of mice. III. H-1 and H-4, two histocompatibility loci in first linkage group. *Immunology* **4**:366-379, 1961.
469. Snell, G. D. Histocompatibility genes of mouse. II. Production and analysis of isogenic resistant lines. *J. Nat. Cancer Inst.* **21**: 843-877, 1958.
470. Allen, S. L. Linkage relations of genes histocompatibility-2 and fused tail, brachyury and kinky tail in mouse, as determined by tumor transplantation. *Genetics* **40**:627-650, 1955.
471. Berrian, J. H., and McKhann, C. F. Transplantation immunity involving H-3 locus: graft survival times. *J. Nat. Cancer Inst.* **25**:111-123, 1960.
472. McKhann, C. F., and Berrian, J. H. Antigenic activity of various tissues in transplantation immunity. *J. Immunol.* **86**:345-353, 1961.
473. Counce, S., Smith, P., Barth, R., and Snell, G. D. Strong and weak histocompatibility genes differences in mice and their role in rejection of homografts of tumors and skin. *Ann. Surg.* **144**: 198-204, 1956.
474. Amos, D. B. Some iso-antigenic systems of mouse. In *Proceedings of the Canadian Cancer Research Conference: Held at Honey Harbour, Ontario, June 17-21, 1958.* Edited by R. W. Bragg. Part 3. 461 pp. New York: Academic Press, 1959. Pp. 241-258.
475. Medawar, P. B. Reactions to homologous tissue antigens in relation to hypersensitivity. In *Cellular and Humoral Aspects of the Hypersensitive State.* Edited by H. S. Lawrence. 683 pp. New York: Harper, 1959. Pp. 504-534.
476. Amos, D. B., Gorer, P. A., and Mikulska, A. B. Analysis of antigenic system in mouse (H-2 system). *Proc. Roy. Soc., London, s. B.* **144**:369-380, 1955.
477. Gorer, P. A., and Mikulska, Z. B. Some further data on H-2 system of antigens. *Proc. Roy. Soc., London, s. B.* **151**:57-69, 1959.
478. Stimpfling, J. H., and Snell, G. D. Histocompatibility genes and some immunogenetic problems. In Symposium on Tissue Transplantation. *Proceedings of the International Symposium on Tissue Transplantation: Held in Vina del mar, Valparaiso in Chile, August 30-September 2, 1961.* Edited by A. P. Christoffanini and G. Hoeker. 269 pp. Santiago de Chile: Universidad de Chile, 1962. Pp. 37-53.

479. Bogden, A. E., and Aptekman, P. M. Histocompatibility antigens and hemagglutinogens in rat. *Ann. New York Acad. Sc.* **97**:43-56, 1962.
480. Schierman, L. W., and Nordskog, A. W. Relationship of blood type to histocompatibility in chickens. *Science* **134**:1008, 1961.
481. Jaffe, W. P., and McDermid, E. M. Blood groups and spleno-megaly in chick embryos. *Science* **137**:984, 1962.
482. Eichwald, E. J. *Transplantation Bull.* **2**:148, 1955.
483. Gittes, R. F., and Russell, P. S. Male histocompatibility antigens in mouse endocrine tissues: functional and histologic evidence. *J. Nat. Cancer Inst.* **26**:283-291, 1961.
484. Bauer, J. A. Genetics of skin transplantation and estimate of number of histocompatibility genes in inbred guinea pigs. *Ann. New York Acad. Sc.* **87**:78-92, 1960.
485. Longmire, W. P., Stone, H B., Daniel, A. S., and Goon, C. D. Report of clinical experience with homografts. *Plast. & Reconstruct. Surg.* **2**:419-426, 1947.
486. Medawar, P. B. Iso-antigens. In Symposium on Biological Problems of Grafting. *Biological Problems of Grafting: A symposium sponsored by the Comm. administrative de Liège and the Council for International Organizations of Medical Sciences.* Edited by F. Albert and P. B. Medawar. 453 pp. Oxford: Blackwell, 1959. Pp. 6-21.
487. Brent, L. Tissue transplantation immunity. *Progr. in Allergy* **5**:271-348, 1958.
488. Hildemann, W. H., and Medawar, P. B. Relationship between skin transplantation immunity and formation of humoral isoantibodies in mice. *Immunology* **2**:44-52, 1959.
489. Brent, L., Medawar, P. B., and Ruszkiewicz, M. Serological methods in study of transplantation antigens. *Brit. J. Exper. Path.* **42**:464-477, 1961.
490. Basch, R. S., and Stetson, C. A. Relationship between hemagglutinogens and histocompatibility antigens in mouse. *Ann. New York Acad. Sc.* **97**:83-94, 1962.
491. Lejeune-Ledant, G. Transplantation antigens, production of haemagglutinins and inhibition of haemagglutination reaction. In *Ciba Foundation Symposium on Transplantation.* Edited by G. E. W. Wolstenholme and M. P. Cameron. 426 pp. Boston: Little, Brown, 1962. Pp. 25-35.
492. Kandutsch, A. A., and Stimpfling, J. H. Isoantigenic lipoprotein from Sarcoma I. In *Ciba Foundation Symposium on Transplantation.* Edited by G. E. W. Wolstenholme and M. P. Cameron. 426 pp. Boston: Little, Brown, 1962. Pp. 72-86.
493. Monaco, A. P., Wood, M. L., and Russell, P. S. Unpublished data.
494. Billingham, R. E. Transplantation immunity and maternal-fetal relation. *New Eng. J. Med.* **270**:667-672 and 720-725, 1964.
495. Krohn, P. Ovarian transplantation in mice. In Symposium on Biological Problems of Grafting. *Biological Problems of Grafting: A symposium sponsored by the Comm. administrative de Liège and the Council for International Organizations of Medical Sciences.* Edited by F. Albert and P. B. Medawar. 453 pp. Oxford: Blackwell, 1959. Pp. 146-157.
496. Linder, O. E. Comparisons between survival of grafted skin, ovaries, and tumors in mice across histocompatibility barriers of different strengths. *J. Nat. Cancer Inst.* **27**:351-373, 1961.
497. Russell, P. S., and Gittes, R. F. Parathyroid transplants in rats: comparison of their survival time with that of skin grafts. *J. Exper. Med.* **109**:571-588, 1959.
498. Simmons, R. L., and Russell, P. S. Antigenicity of mouse trophoblast. *Ann. New York Acad. Sc.* **99**:717-732, 1962.
499. Barth, R. F., and Russell, P. S. The antigenic specificity of spermatozoa. *J. Immunol.* **93**:13-19, 1964.

500. Billingham, R. E., Brent, L., and Medawar, P. B. Antigenic stimulus in transplantation immunity. *Nature* (London) **178**:514-519, 1956.
501. Chutná, T., and Hašková, V. Antigenicity of embryonic tissues in homotransplantation. *Folia biol.* **5**:85-88, 1959.
502. Pizzaro, O., Hoecker, G., Rubinstein, P., and Ramos, A. Distribution in tissues and development of H-2 antigens of mouse. *Proc. Nat. Acad. Sc.* **47**:1900-1907, 1961.
503. Mitchison, N. A. Effect on offspring of maternal immunization in mice. *J. Genet.* **51**:406-420, 1953.
504. Möller, G. Studies on development of isoantigens of H-2 system in newborn mice. *J. Immunol.* **86**:56-68, 1961.
505. *Idem.* Differentiation of H-2 isoantigens in newborn and embryonic mice. *Transplantation Bull.* **29**:144, 1962.
506. Doria, G. Development of hemotransplantation antigens in mouse hemopoietic tissues. *Transplantation* **1**:311-317, 1963.
507. Monad, J., and Jacob, F. General conclusion: teleonomic mechanism in cellular metabolism, growth and differentiation. In *Cold Spring Harbor Symp., Quant. Biol.* **26**:389-401, 1961.
508. Basch, R. S., and Stetson, C. A. Quantitative studies on histocompatibility antigens of mouse. *Transplantation* **1**:469-480, 1963.
509. Barnes, A. D. Quantitative comparative study of immunizing ability of different tissues. *Ann. New York Acad. Sc.* (in press).
510. Basch, R., and Stetson, C. A., Jr. Quantitative *in vitro* assay of murine isoantigens. *Federation Proc.* **20**:39, 1961.
511. Breyere, E. J. Effect of prior inoculation of packed erythrocytes on survival of skin homografts in rats. *Proc. Soc. Exper. Biol. & Med.* **101**:744-747, 1959.
512. Möller, G. Demonstration of mouse isoantigens at cellular level by fluorescent antibody technique. *J. Exper. Med.* **114**:415-434, 1961.
513. Oth, A., and Castermans, A. Study of transplantation antigens from isolated nuclei. *Transplantation Bull.* **6**:418-424, 1959.
514. Medawar. P. B. Part played by deoxyribonucleic acid in transplantation immunity. *Nature* (London) **182**:62, 1958.
515. Hašková, V., and Hrubešová, M. Part played by deoxyribonucleic acid in transplantation immunity. *Nature* (London) **182**:61, 1958.
516. Hager, E., DuPuy, M., and Wallach, D. Immunologic suicide and studies on the role of antibody and complement in canine kidney homograft rejection. *Ann. New York Acad. Sc.* **120**:447-457, 1964.
517. Ebbe, S., Baldini, M., and Dameshek, W. Antigenic structure of blood platelets. II. Histocompatibility antigens in rabbit blood platelets. *Blood* **19**:548-556, 1962.
518. Wilson, D. B. Influence of host's sex on induction of tolerance of homologous tissues. *Transplantation* **1**:79-82, 1963.
519. Herzenberg, L. A., and Herzenberg, L. A. Association of H-2 antigens with cell membrane fraction of mouse liver. *Proc. Nat. Acad. Sc.* **47**:762-767, 1961.
520. Kandutsch, A. A. Intracellular distribution and extraction of tumor homograft-enhancing antigens. *Cancer Research* **20**:264-268, 1960.
521. Dumonde, D. C., Al-Askari, S., Lawrence, H. S., and Thomas, L. Microsomal fractions as transplantation antigens. *Nature* (London) **198**:598, 1963.
522. Sanderson, A. R., and Davies, D. A. L. Enzymatic activity of mouse histocompatibility antigen preparations. *Nature* (London) **200**:32, 1963.
523. Manson, L. A., Foschi, G. V., and Palm, J. *In vivo* and *in vitro* studies of histocompatibility antigens isolated from cultured mouse cell line. *Proc. Nat. Acad. Sc.* **48**:1816-1822, 1962.

524. *Idem.* Association of transplantation antigens with microsomal lipoproteins of normal and malignant mouse tissues. *J. Cell. & Comp. Physiol.* **61**:109-118, 1963.

525. Monaco, A. P., Wood, M. L., and Russell, P. S. A simple method for the preparation of cell-free antigens. Physical and biological properties. *S. Forum* **15**:133-135, 1964.

526. Brent, L., Medawar, P. B., and Ruszkiewicz, M. Studies on transplantation antigens. In *Ciba Foundation Symposium on Transplantation.* Edited by G. E. W. Wolstenholme and M. P. Cameron. 426 pp. Boston: Little, Brown, 1962. Pp. 6-20.

527. Billingham, R. E., Brent, L., and Medawar, P. B. Extraction of antigens causing transplantation immunity. *Transplantation Bull.* **5**:377-381, 1958.

528. Davies, D. A. Isolation of mouse antigens carrying H-2 histocompatibility specificity: some preliminary studies. *Biochem. J.* **84**:307-317, 1962.

529. *Idem.* Purification and chemical composition of mouse histocompatibility antigen. *Ann. New York Acad. Sc.* **101**:114-120, 1962.

530. *Idem.* Chemical nature of mouse histocompatibility antigens. *Nature* (London) **193**:34-36, 1962.

531. *Idem.* Presence of non-H-2 histocompatibility specificities in preparations of mouse H-2 antigens. *Transplantation* **1**:562-568, 1963.

532. *Idem.* H-2 histocompatibility antigens of mouse. In *Ciba Foundation Symposium on Transplantation.* Edited by G. E. W. Wolstenholme and M. P. Cameron. 426 pp. Boston: Little, Brown, 1962. Pp. 45-65.

533. Kandutsch, A. A., and Stimpfling, J. H. Partial purification of tissue isoantigens from mouse sarcoma. *Transplantation* **1**:201-216, 1963.

534. *Idem.* Isoantigenic lipoprotein from sarcoma I. In *Ciba Foundation Symposium on Transplantation.* Edited by G. E. W. Wolstenholme and M. P. Cameron. 426 pp. Boston: Little, Brown, 1962. Pp. 72-86.

535. Kaliss, N. Survival of homografts in mice pretreated with antisera to mouse tissue. *Ann. New York Acad. Sc.* **64**:977-990, 1957.

536. Mandel, M. A., Monaco, A. P., and Russell, P. S. Unpublished data.

537. Harbison, S. P., and Fisher, B. In *The Contributions of Dr. C. C. Guthrie to Vascular Surgery.* 360 pp. Pittsburgh: Univ. of Pittsburgh Press, 1959.

538. Hardy, J. D., Eraslan, S., and Dalton, M. L., Jr. Autotransplantation and homotransplantation of lung: further studies. *J. Thoracic & Cardiovas. Surg.* **46**:606-615, 1963.

539. Reemtsma, K., Rogers, R. F., Lucas, J. F., Schmidt, F. E., and Davis, F. H., Jr. Studies of pulmonary function in transplantation of canine lung. *J. Thoracic & Cardiovas. Surg.* **46**:589-597, 1963.

540. Barnes, B. A., Flax, M. H., Barr, G., and Burke, J. F. Experimental pulmonary homografts in dog. I. Morphological studies. *Transplantation* **1**:351-364, 1963.

541. Barnes, B. A., and Flax, M. H. Experimental pulmonary homografts in dog. II. Modification of homograft response by BW 57-322, *Transplantation* **2**:343-356, 1964.

542. Goodrich, E. O., Jr., Welch, H. F., Nelson, J., Beecher, T., and Welch, C. S. Homotransplantation of canine liver. *Surgery* **39**:244-251, 1956.

543. Starzl, T. E., Kaupp, H. A., Jr., Brock, D. R., Lazarus, R. E., and Johnson, R. V. Reconstructive problems in canine liver homotransplantation with special reference to post-operative role of hepatic venous flow. *Surg., Gynec. & Obst.* **111**:733-743, 1960.

544. Moore, F. D., et al. Experimental whole-organ transplantation of liver and of spleen. *Ann. Surg.* **152**:374-387, 1960.

545. Starzl, T. E., Kaupp, H. A., Jr., Brock, D. R., and Linman, J. W. Studies on rejection of transplanted homologous dog liver. *Surg., Gynec. & Obst.* **112**:135-144, 1961.

546. Wheeler, H. B., et al. Homograft response to whole-organ transplantation of canine spleen. *J. S. Research* **2**:114-123, 1962.

547. Montague, A. C. W., Greenberg, J. B., Dammin, G. J., and Moore, F. D. Effect of nitrogen mustard in altering histocompatibility rejection sequence in splenic homotransplantation in dog. *J. S. Research* **2**:130-135, 1962.

548. Fisher, B., Lee, S. H., and Fisher, E. R. Observations concerning spleen homotransplantation in normal and irradiated animals. *Surg., Gynec. & Obst.* **112**:455-462, 1961.

549. Calne, R. Y. *Renal Transplantation: Foreword by J. E. Murray.* 151 pp. Baltimore: Williams & Wilkins, 1963.

550. Mayerson, H. S. Lymphatic system with particular reference to kidney. *Surg., Gynec. & Obst.* **116**:259-272, 1963.

551. Chiba, C., et al. Studies on transplanted heart: its metabolism and histology. *J. Exper. Med.* **115**:853-866, 1962.

552. Ramos, H. R., et al. Presence of humoral factors in heart homograft rejection of transplanted heart. *Transplantation* **1**:284-292, 1963.

553. Blumenstock, D., et al. Prolonged survival of orthotopic homotransplants of heart in animals treated with methotrexate. *J. Thoracic & Cardiovas. Surg.* **46**:616-628, 1963.

554. Mack, J. R., Nathan, P., Wexler, B. C., Gonzalez, E., and Miller, B. F. Homotransplantation of dog jejunum. *Transplantation Bull.* **25**:391-394, 1960.

555. Lillehei, R. C., Longerbeam, J. K., and Scott, W. R. Whole organ grafts of stomach. *J.A.M.A.* **183**:861-865, 1963.

556. Lillehei, R. C. Techniques of organ transplantation by direct vascular anastomoses. In *Research Methods in Surgery.* Edited by W. F. Ballinger, II. 368 pp. Boston: Little, Brown, 1964. Pp. 281-325.

557. Newth, D. R. Chance compatibility in homografting. *Transplantation Bull.* **27**:452-455, 1961.

558. Rapaport, F. T., Thomas, L., Converse, J. M., and Lawrence, H. S. Variations in individual specificity in human homograft reaction. *Federation Proc.* **20**:36, 1960.

559. Wilson, R. E., Henry, L., and Merrill, J. P. Model system for determining histocompatibility in man. *J. Clin. Investigation* **42**: 1497-1503, 1963.

560. Matsukura, M., Mery, A. M., Amiel, J. L., and Mathé, G. Investigation on test of histocompatibility for allogeneic grafts. II. Study on rabbits. *Transplantation* **1**:61-64, 1963.

561. Brent, L. Some remarks on present state of problem of tissue typing. In National Research Council. *Proceedings of Conference and Workshop on Tissue Histocompatibility Testing.* Edited by P. S. Russell, H. Winn and D. B. Amos. Washington, D. C.: The Council (in press).

562. Brent, L., and Medawar, P. B. Tissue transplantation: new approach to "typing" problem. *Brit. M. J.* **2**:269-272, 1963.

563. Gray, J. G., and Russell, P. S. Donor selection in human organ transplantation: possible screening test. *Lancet* **2**:863-865, 1963.

564. Gray, J. G. Lymphocyte transfer test in man. In *Proceedings of Conference and Workshop on Tissue Histocompatibility Testing.*[561]

565. Bach, F., and Hirschhorn, K. Lymphocyte interaction: potential histocompatibility test *in vitro. Science* **143**:813, 1964.

566. Bain, B., Vos, M. R., and Lowenstein, L. Development of large immature mononuclear cells in mixed leukocyte cultures. *Blood* **23**:108-116, 1964.

567. Bain, B., Lowenstein, L., and MacLean, L. D. In vitro "mixed leukocyte reaction" and initial studies in its application as test for histocompatibility. In *Proceedings of Conference and Workshop on Tissue Histocompatibility Testing*.[561]

568. Van Rood, J. J., and van Leeuwen, A. Leukocyte grouping: method and its application. *J. Clin. Investigation* **42**:1382-1390, 1963.

569. *Idem.* Defined leukocyte antigenic groups in men. In *Proceedings of Conference and Workshop on Tissue Histocompatibility Testing*.[561]

570. Payne, R., Tripp, M., Weigle, J., Bodmer, W., and Bodmer, J. New leukocyte isoantigen system in man. In *Cold Spring Harbor Symp. Quant. Biol.* (in press).

571. Schatten, W. E., Bloom, W. L., and Hamm, W. G. Effects of endocrine homografts on thyroid and parathyroid function. *Surg., Gynec. & Obst.* **112**:196-202, 1961.

572. Dunphy, J. E., and Jacob, S. W. "Successful" implantation of heterologous parathyroid tissue in man. *New Eng. J. Med.* **264**: 371-374, 1961.

573. Sanderson, P. H., Marshall, F., II, and Wilson, R. E. Calcium and phosphorus homeostasis in parathyroidectomized dog: evaluation by means of ethylenediamine tetraacetate and calcium tolerance tests. *J. Clin. Investigation* **39**:662-670, 1960.

574. Watkins, E., Jr., Haynes, L. L., and Adams, H. D. Aortic-pedicle technique for obtaining immediate vascularization of fetal parathyroid-gland transplants in man: application in three patients with hypoparathyroidism appearing after thyroidectomy. *New Eng. J. Med.* **261**:105-112, 1959.

575. Sterling, J. A., and Goldsmith, R. Total transplant of thyroid gland using vascular anastomosis: report of successful result in chronic tetany. *Surgery* **35**:624-628, 1954.

576. Brooks, J. R., Sturgis, S. H., and Hill, G. J. Evaluation of endocrine tissue homotransplantation in Millipore chamber: with note on tissue adaptation to host. *Ann. New York Acad. Sc.* **87**:482-500, 1960.

577. Bassett, C. A. L., and Campbell, J. B. Calcification of Millipore in vivo. *Transplantation Bull.* **26**:132, 1960.

578. Broster, L. R., and Gardiner-Hill, H. Case of Addison's disease successfully treated by graft. *Brit. M. J.* **2**:570-572, 1946.

579. Carnevali, J. F., ReMine, W. H., Grindlay, J. H., and Harrison, E. G., Jr. Experiences with autotransplantation of islet-cell tissue in dogs. *Arch. Surg.* **81**:708-714, 1960.

580. Kay, G. D. Prolonged survival of skin homograft in patient with very extensive burns. *Ann. New York Acad. Sc.* **64**:767-774, 1957.

581. Thomas, E. D., Lochte, H. L., Jr., Cannon, J. H., Sahler, O. P., and Ferrebee, J. W. Supralethal whole body irradiation and isologous marrow transplantation in man. *J. Clin. Investigation* **38**:1709-1716, 1959.

582. McGovern, J. J., Russell, P. S., Atkins, L., and Webster, E. W. Treatment of terminal leukemic relapse by total-body irradiation and intravenous infusion of stored autologous bone marrow obtained during remission. *New Eng. J. Med.* **260**:675-683, 1959.

583. Clifford, P., Clift, R. A., and Duff, J. K. Nitrogen-mustard therapy combined with autologous marrow infusion. *Lancet* **1**: 687-690, 1961.

584. Mills, S. D., Kyle, R. A., Hallenbek, G. A., Pease, G. L., and Cree, I. C. Bone-marrow transplant in identical twin. *J.A.M.A.* **188**:1037-1040, 1964.

585. Thomas, E. D., Phillips, J. H., and Finch, C. A. Recovery from marrow failure following isogenic marrow infusion. *J.A.M.A.* **188**: 1041-1043, 1964.

586. Mathé, G., et al. Transfusions et greffes de moelle osseuse homologue chez des humains irradiés à haute dose accidentellement. *Rev. franç. clin. biol.* **4**:226-238, 1959.
587. Thomas, E. D., Lochte, H. L., Jr., and Ferrebee, J. W. Irradiation of entire body and marrow transplantation: some observations and comments. *Blood* **14**:1-23, 1959.
588. Huarani, F. I., Repplinger, E., and Tocantins, L. M. Attempts at transplantation of human bone marrow in patients with acute leukemia and other marrow depletion disorders. *Am. J. Med.* **28**:794-806, 1960.
589. Mathé, G., et al. Essai de traitement de sujets atteints de leucémie aiguë en rémission par irradiation totale suivie de transfusion de moelle osseuse homologue. *Rev. franç. clin. biol.* **4**:675-704, 1959.
590. Mathé, G., et al. Nouveaux essais de greffe de moelle osseuse homologue après irradiation totale chez des enfants atteints de leucémie aiguë en rémission: le problème de syndrome secondaire chez l'homme. *Rev. d'hémat.* **15**:115-161, 1960.
591. Mathé, G., Amiel, J. L., Schwarzenberg, L., Cattan, A., and Schneider, M. Haematopoietic chimaera in man after allogenic (homologous) bone-marrow transplantation: control secondary syndrome: specific tolerance due to chimerism. *Brit. M. J.* **2**:1633-1635, 1963.
592. Hardy, J. D., Webb, W. R., Dalton, M. L., Jr., and Walker, G. R., Jr. Lung homotransplantation in man. *J.A.M.A.* **186**:1065-1074, 1963.
593. Magovern, G. J., and Yates, A. J. Homotransplantation of left lung: report of case. *Ann. New York Acad. Sc.* **120**:710-728, 1964.
594. Starzl, T. E., Marchioro, T. L., and Waddell, W. R. Experimental and clinical homotransplantation of liver. *Ann. New York Acad. Sc.* **120**:739-765, 1964.
595. Moore, F. D., et al. Immunosuppression and vascular insufficiency in liver transplantation. *Ann. New York Acad. Sc.* **120**:729-738, 1964.
596. Marchioro, T. L., Starzl, T. E., and Waddell, W. R. Splenic homotransplantation. *Ann. New York Acad. Sc.* **120**:626-651, 1964.
597. Hardy, J. D., et al. Heart transplantation in man: developmental studies and report of case. *J.A.M.A.* **188**:1132-1140, 1964.
598. Malt, R. A., and McKhann, C. F. Replantation of severed arms. *J.A.M.A.* **189**:716-722, 1964.
599. Unger, E. Nierentransplantationen. *Berl. klin. Wchnschr.* **47**:573-578, 1910.
600. Hume, D. M., Merrill, J. P., Miller, B. F., and Thorn, G. W. Experiences with renal homotransplantation in human: report of 9 cases. *J. Clin. Investigation* **34**:327-382, 1955.
601. Merrill, J. P., Murray, J. E., Harrison, J. H., and Guild, W. R. Successful homotransplantation of human kidney between identical twins. *J.A.M.A.* **160**:277-282, 1956.
602. Murray, J. E., Gleason, R., and Bartholomay, A. Human kidney transplantation. Second report of registry. **2**:660-667, 1964.
603. Merrell, M., and Shulman, L. E. Determination of prognosis in chronic disease, illustrated by systemic lupus erythematosus. *J. Chronic Dis.* **1**:12, 1955.
604. Greenwood, M. Reports on public health and statistical subjects, No. 33. A report on the natural duration of cancer. Appendix 1. The errors of sampling of the survivorship tables. London: His Majesty's Stationery Office, 1926.
605. Murray, J. E., and Harrison, J. H. Surgical management of fifty patients with kidney transplants including eighteen pairs of twins. *Am. J. Surg.* **105**:205-218, 1963.

606. Kirkpatrick, C. H., Wilson, W., and Talmage, D. Immunologic studies in human organ transplantation. *J. Exper. Med.* **119**: 727-742, 1964.
607. Flax, M. H. Experimental allergic thyroiditis in guinea pig. II. Morphologic studies of development of disease. *Lab. Investigation* **12**:199-213, 1963.
608. Dempster, W. J. Reassessment of anurias after kidney transplantation. *Brit. M. J.* **1**:1697-1701, 1963.
609. Terasaki, P., Akiyama, T., McClelland, J. D., and Cannon, J. A. Renal damage produced *in vivo* by homologous mouse antisera. *Ann. New York Acad. Sc.* **99**:645-656, 1962.
610. Porter, K. A., et al. Obliterative vascular changes in four human kidney homotransplants. *Brit. M. J.* **2**:639, 1963.
611. Reemtsma, K., et al. Reversal of early graft rejection after renal heterotransplantation in man. *J.A.M.A.* **187**:691-696, 1964.
612. Merrill, J. P. Personal communication.

INDEX

Index

P 55

Prepare inoperable
C+D pts